SURGEON

Should he report the incompetent doctor who almost killed his patient by operating for the wrong ailment?

How could he tell the distracted parents that their bright seven-year-old son had become a living vegetable as the result of a necessary operation?

Would his wife understand that he *couldn't* come home that night, or his own guilt would have overwhelmed him?

If he played dirty politics, could he win the fellowship?

A hard-hitting, unsparing story of the making of a surgeon, the risks he must take with his patients' lives, the politics he must play to save his own!

SURGEON

"Dr. Bowman"

▲ PYRAMID BOOKS • NEW YORK

SURGEON

A PYRAMID BOOK
Published by arrangement with Parallax Publishing Co.

First printing September, 1966
Second printing August, 1971

PYRAMID BOOKS are published by Pyramid Publications
A Division of Pyramid Communications, Inc.
444 Madison Avenue, New York, New York 10022, U.S.A.

Introduction

THIS BOOK is a recollection. By that I mean that it is
not a day by day account culled from a diary, but,
rather, a series of remembered events, sometimes
loosely connected. It covers my fifth year as a resident
in Surgery. However, since that year ended so recently,
perhaps "recollection" is not the most fitting term, suggesting as it does a reminiscence, a calling back of
happenings from the distant past. If the reader chooses,
then, he may think of what follows as a report. Or,
with my wife, Sue, he may regard it as a catharsis.
But in the latter instance the reader should smile—as
Sue does.

Be that as it may, the events which are recounted in
this book *did* happen. The details remained in my
mind. And now they have been gathered and put on
paper. The hope is that they will inform and edify.

I cannot claim that what occurred to me during
my fifth year as a surgical resident is wholly typical.
In fact, I suspect that the particular situation in
which I was involved is quite uncommon. But the
background against which this drama—if you will—
was played is not. Briggs Memorial Hospital is much
like any other private hospital in any other metro-
politan center. The patients and the medical staff are
also fairly representative.

Being both the narrator of and a participant in this

story, I realize—and perhaps the reader should take this fact into account—that I have an advantage. I could, if I chose, remember things as I wanted to remember them, not necessarily as they truly occurred. I hope I have not tumbled into that trap. I have tried not to. In the first draft of the book there were instances where I interpreted the actions of others, assigning motives. But these instances were challenged—by Sue, who bombarded me with "How do you know?" and "Are you sure about this?" and "Who appointed you God?" until I begged for mercy. As a consequence, such interpretations have been exorcised, and I attempt to tell only "what" happened, not "why"—unless, of course, I am describing an act of my own. Any other judging that is done will have to be done by the reader—may he be omniscient.

Nothing else, however, has been edited out of this book. There has been no attempt to romanticize either surgery—which is, at base, a detailed and exhausting business—or surgeons. There are no blue-eyed, square-jawed heroes here—only people. Men with narrow limits and men with broad limits. Misfits. A doctor whose ability far out-reached the recognition he received. Incompetents. And all those who quietly performed their duties, seeking nothing but the satisfaction of a job well done. Combined, these people made mistakes. And I have let the mistakes stand. But combined, too, they won victories. And these also I have let stand. There are more victories here than there are mistakes. But that is only because that is the way it was.

Finally, the names of the people involved have been changed. For some, that is a kindness. But in all cases it is a necessity—for the lawyers, in their wisdom, insist.

DOCTOR BOWMAN

One

My FOURTH year of residency was behind me. The two weeks of vacation that followed were also over. Now, I pushed through the revolving door of the apartment building where married residents were quartered and stepped out onto the street that separated the building from the several others that made up the complex called Briggs Memorial Hospital. Behind me, asleep in our three-and-a-half-room apartment, I left my wife, Sue, and our son, Peter, aged two. This was the first day of my fifth year.

It was a few minutes after six in the morning. Before Peter had been born, Sue usually got up when I did and prepared breakfast for me. But Peter had proved to be a restless child, rousing Sue from sleep at least once every night. So we had decided that she would sleep in the morning, and that I would get my breakfasts at the hospital cafeteria. It worked no particular hardship on me.

I entered the hospital through the front door, crossed the reception area, which was deserted except for a guard at the desk, then rode the elevator to a subbasement, where the cafeteria was located. Business was not brisk that morning. There were no more than a dozen interns and residents at the tables. I picked up a tray and silverware and got what passed for scrambled eggs, buttered toast, and coffee, then sat by myself near the cash register.

7

I wanted to be alone to think. My fifth year as a surgical resident was not going to begin as routinely as I had supposed. While I had been away on vacation, a monkey wrench, so to speak, had been tossed into the works.

I had learned about this the night before. Sue and I and Peter had arrived back at the apartment in the late afternoon, after a twelve-hour drive from my hometown, where we had spent the previous two weeks. Peter was cranky. Sue was determinedly cheerful—a forced mood she dons just before she explodes. And I was grumbling and muttering, wondering why in God's name any sane man would ever get married and have children.

After Peter had been coaxed to bed for a nap with a threat of physical violence, Sue began the unpacking and I collapsed in a chair with a beer. At that moment, the doorbell rang. I answered it. It was George Bruner, a fellow fifth-year resident, who, with his wife, Marge, and two children, had an apartment on the same floor. The Bruners, apparently, had heard us come banging in.

George was large—something over six feet—and bearish. The backs of his hands and forearms were covered with a blanket of black curly hair. He had an expression that was permanently antagonistic. But, paradoxically, he was probably the most gentle, good-natured man I had ever met. And, as a doctor, that was one of his limitations. He could not bring himself to cause pain. In some other profession or trade, that would have been admirable. But for a doctor it was a handicap, since pain must be used as a guide, an indicator. And to avoid it, to shy away from it, is to do the patient a disservice.

I got a beer for George, and he asked me about our

8

trip, and I began telling him about it. Sue came in and settled in a chair and—still being doggedly cheerful—corrected nearly every statement I made. This was not her usual self. She had spent two weeks on her best behavior for the benefit of my parents, and she was resolved to punish me for it. I expected that once George left we would have words. But as far as I was concerned, they would be welcome. For after that, we would apologize to each other, relax, and resume our normal way of life.

As it happened, that is *not* the way it happened.

George abruptly switched the conversation to the hospital. "We've had some action back here, too," he said. "Gar is out."

When I had left, Dr. Maxwell Gar had been the acting head of surgery. It was assumed by almost everyone that he would be named to that post permanently. It was a logical assumption. He had been associated with Briggs for years. He was respected. And he had been the assistant head of surgery under Dr. Marquette. When Dr. Marquette retired and Gar was named acting head, it was naturally thought that that was simply the first step in his promotion.

"Out?" I said. "Out how?"

"Not out," George said. "I mean they put him back to Assistant and brought in a new man to be Head."

"Who?"

"His name is Clover. Boston."

I knew whom he meant. "Wilson Clover," I said.

"That's right."

Dr. Wilson Clover was a familiar name to me. His by-line had appeared on a substantial number of the papers and articles on open-heart surgery I had read. He had developed many open-heart techniques himself and had perfected many others. If there was a

9

"name" in open-heart surgery at the time, it was Wilson Clover.

"I guess it's quite a catch for Briggs," Bruner said.

"And quite a lump for Dr. Gar," Sue commented. She spoke softly, a little sadly. The bite had gone out of her tone. I realized that we would not be having words that night. Her sympathy for Dr. Gar—and possibly the realization of the effect the turn of events might have on me—had overwhelmed her desire to go into battle.

"What about Gar?" I said. "How is he taking it?"

"I don't know," Bruner replied. "We just heard the rumor this morning. It won't be official until tomorrow."

And that was the hub around which my thoughts were turning as I sat at the table in the cafeteria the next morning. By then, my concern had centered on myself. How would the replacement of Dr. Gar by Dr. Clover affect me?

If I had been ready to go into practice, the effect would have been nil. But there was a fellowship at stake. And the fellowship was in open-heart surgery. As matters stood when I left on vacation, there were five fifth-year surgical residents in competition for this plum—myself, George Bruner, Tris Maney, Lou Manx, and Paul Brandt. In theory, at least, there were five in the competition. But, in fact, it was generally realized that the race was between myself and Paul Brandt. And, then, I had been leading.

My advantage had been due to the fact that Dr. Gar was acting head of surgery. It was Dr. Gar who, in that position, would make the decision. And there was reason to believe that Dr. Gar favored me. Not that he showed the favoritism—if, indeed, it did exist. But it was logically assumed that he would choose me over

Brandt—all other elements being equal—for the reason that I, like Gar himself, was more interested in practice than in research.

Now that advantage was gone. Dr. Clover—not Dr. Gar—would decide who got the fellowship. And Dr. Clover's primary interest was in research—as was Paul Brandt's. Logic told me that the advantage I had lost had been picked up by Brandt. Although this was not necessarily so. In fact, we all might find ourselves running against a new competitor. Dr. Clover undoubtedly had a wide acquaintanceship. He might have someone else in mind for the fellowship—someone from Boston, say?

Leaving most of my breakfast, I left the cafeteria and took the elevator to the sixth floor—the lower of the four surgical floors—to report in. There, I was told by the clerk that the surgical residents had been called to a meeting in the sixth-floor auditorium (a grand term for a small room) and that I was probably already late.

"You're meeting the new Head," she informed me as I hurried out.

As it happened, it was the principals, not I, who were late. When I reached the auditorium it was packed with first-, second-, third-, fourth-, and fifth-year residents (the interns had been stuck with floor duty), but no one in any authority had yet arrived. I saw George Bruner and Lou Manx standing together and joined them.

Lou Manx was a tall, slender, good-looking boy from New York. No matter what happened, he was usually amused by it. Most people thought that he was incapable of taking anything seriously, but I suspect that he had simply made peace with the inevitable at an

11

earlier age than most of us, that he refused to suffer over things he knew he could not change.

Manx was without a doubt the best diagnostician among the surgical residents. He had, as they say, the knack. It was almost a sixth sense, an antenna that vibrated at the very moment when an illness or disease gave a hint of its nature or hiding place. And he could apply this talent not only to patients but also to lay situations. When there was an undercurrent about, Manx knew it. Unfortunately, he also had an annoying habit of describing it to his friends.

"You here?" he said. "I thought you'd be out front—demonstrating. Carrying a sign. 'Clover Go Home'."

"I brought a bomb," I said. "The minute Clover gets here, *blooey*, the whole joint goes up in smoke."

The conversation remained on Clover—speculation on what kind of a guy he would be, respectful comments on his background. All guessing about Dr. Gar's reaction had apparently been done the day before.

With my mind only half on what was being said, I looked around the auditorium. I saw Paul Brandt with Tris Maney. Brandt could close a person out. And he was doing that now to Maney. He could stand facing you, in conversation with you, outwardly intent on what you were saying, yet, in fact, be miles away. You weren't aware of this until you got to know him. Then, you would notice that his eyes weren't quite focusing on you. They were looking past you—straight through you—at something invisible beyond.

It wasn't a conscious discourtesy. Brandt had a quick and indefatigable mind and a low threshold of boredom. He usually knew completely what you were going to say after you had finished the first sentence of your story. Rather than force his attention to remain on what he knew was coming, he turned it to something else—using the time for something important (to him)—until you had finally finished what you had to say.

The habit wasn't offensive, though. Probably because, in other ways, Brandt was marvelously likable. He had a vast enthusiasm for his work—that part of it, at least, that centered on research—and he communicated a kind of mature optimism about life in general. He believed—it seemed—that with diligence he could make anything come out right, and, in his company, you very nearly believed the same thing. On top of that he was physically attractive, in a male kind of way. He was tall, well-built, and dark, with close-cropped black hair. His face was squarish, his features sharply defined. All in all, he looked solid, dependable. And he was.

Tris Maney, on the other hand, was almost the exact opposite. Watching him, I saw his mouth going a mile a minute. Without being able to hear what he was saying, I knew that he was whining. Society, to hear Maney tell it, had picked him as its ultimate victim. Anything adverse, or even simply irritating, that happened was a result not of chance, but of a preconceived and malicious plot against him.

His attitude evidently had shaped his physical development. He had the look and manner of a victim. He was frail, bony, and stooped. And his eyes were never still, darting here and there, expecting, looking for, the next attack.

It was understandable that Brandt had closed him out. Maney was a cross. Unkind as it may be to say it without some qualification, the simple fact of the matter is: Maney was a bore, without one single saving grace that I ever detected.

In time—about five minutes after I arrived—the

powers finally appeared. Dr. Mackey, the president of the hospital, entered first. As usual, he appeared to be running a half-hour behind schedule and desperate to catch up. Dr. Mackey did not walk—or even run—anywhere. He plunged. But it seemed to agree with him. At age seventy he was probably the healthiest person in the hospital. He had never spent any time there as a patient.

Dr. Mackey was followed by a stranger—Dr. Clover, as we soon learned. Clover was somewhat of a surprise. He was of medium height, and rather tubby. He wore rimless spectacles. His hair was going fast on top, and was salt-and-pepper gray at the sides. He did not look like an outstanding surgeon—or like any kind of surgeon. If anything, he looked like the secretary of the Plunketville Chamber of Commerce.

Behind Clover came Dr. Gar. He looked sour. But that was no indication of how he felt. He always looked sour, like a man who had just tasted bile. This was not his manner, however, only his expression. As a person he was even-tempered and mild-speaking and patient—sometimes to a point beyond belief. It is possible that his sour expression was a result of keeping such excellent control over his emotions. The exertion of that much will—continuously—would, I think, turn most men a little acid.

The trio mounted the brief rise that served as a stage. Dr. Mackey made a few appropriate remarks. We were probably aware, he told us, that a new head of surgery was to be appointed. He wanted us—the surgical residents—to meet the new man before the official announcement was made. He touched here and there on Dr. Clover's background, and then gestured toward our new head of surgery, and Dr. Clover stepped forward.

14

Clover's remarks, too, were brief. But he made an impression. Not by what he said, but by the way in which he said it. He had presence. The instant he took the floor, the secretary of the Plunketville Chamber of Commerce disappeared, and the famous doctor stood in his place. It was obvious now that he was *more* than a surgeon, *more* than a researcher, he was the Man at the Top. By his manner, he informed us that we were at various levels below him. And that we could approach him, but that we could come only so close, and not one step nearer.

This was not stated—his remarks, as I recall, were ambiguous—but it was made eloquently clear. And, I think, it was appreciated. We had enough problems. We did not want a weak or indecisive man at the top to add to them. Our first impression was that the new head of surgery suited us just fine.

Dr. Clover next gave a generous nod to his assistant —Dr. Gar. He praised Dr. Gar for the way he had carried out his duties as acting head, and spoke of his mammoth respect for the older man's ability as a surgeon—commenting that Gar's practical experience far outshone his own. He was grateful that Dr. Gar had promised to continue in his previous capacity as Assistant.

Dr. Gar merely continued to look sour.

The official part of the meeting ended then. Dr. Mackey took off—frantic to catch up—for parts unknown. Dr. Gar forced a few smiles, made an excuse, then departed on Dr. Mackey's heels. And the residents crowded around the new head of surgery—at his invitation—to say a few words to him personally.

George Bruner disappeared into the crowd. I saw Paul Brandt and Tris Maney follow him. But Lou Manx and I held back.

"Will he remember me if I shake his hand and tell him what an honor it's going to be to work under him?" Manx mused. He shook his head. "Why should he? All the others will be doing and saying the same thing."

"I think I'll go up to the floor," I said. "I have two weeks catching up to do."

"You better stay and get a lick in," Manx said. "Brandt is over there."

"I'll meet him," I said.

We left the auditorium and walked down the corridor toward the elevators.

"I wonder if Gar went to get his wound treated," Manx said.

"His what?"

"His back wound," Manx smiled. "Clover put the knife in—I figure—about a quarter of an inch. Enough to need a Band-Aid."

I thought Clover had handled the matter well, praising Gar, and I said so.

"It was unnecessary," Manx said. "Gar didn't need it. We know he's a hot-shot. He's got the practice to prove it. Clover was putting him in his place. He was the Head of Surgery tossing a few candy-coated crumbs to an Assistant. You don't do that to an equal—and in surgery Gar is at least his equal. You do that to subordinates, but not to equals."

"Gar is under him," I pointed out.

"Only on a list," Manx said. "And only right here, inside these walls. But anywhere else, and in the profession, when it comes to status, Gar is, as I said before, at least Clover's equal."

"They'll get along," I said. "Gar can get along with anybody."

16

"It isn't Gar's choice. You saw Clover. Is he the kind who wants an equal under him?"

I saw what Manx meant. Clover had struck me as the kind who would prefer to have everyone he worked with several rungs down the ladder.

"He'll work it," Manx said. "I'll give it six months, then Gar will resign. He'll say the job's interfering with his practice."

I wouldn't have bet a lot of money on it—either way. Even if I'd had a lot of money.

"He'll start crowding Gar—in little ways," Manx said. "Overruling him, maybe. Rejecting his advice. Treating him not as a colleague, but as a subordinate. It'll tell. It'll get under Gar's skin. So, he'll bow out. Gracefully, but out."

Without much to go on, I suspected that Manx might be right. I respected his antenna.

We reached the elevators and got aboard an up car.

"I'll bet you a breakfast on it," Manx said. "And I'll give it six months."

I took the bet. But only to get Manx off the subject. I didn't want to hear any more about it. It bothered me—mightily. I just realized that one bit of advice that Dr. Clover might reject would be Dr. Gar's recommendation on the open-heart fellowship. It didn't exactly make the first day of my fifth year in surgery a banner one.

Two

WHEN MANX and I reached the floor, we separated. He had an early scrub. I went to the desk where the schedule was posted, and found that, uncharacteristically, I was not due in the operating room for another hour and a half. I used the time, first, to go over the work-ups—the histories and physicals—of the patients I was scheduled to have that day, then, secondly, to inspect the charts of the patients I had operated on before I went on vacation. Of those still in the hospital all were coming along as expected, some recovering, some creeping or racing toward death.

When my time ran out, I went to the tenth floor—the operating floor. I was scheduled to scrub on the first case with Dr. Carl Weaver. He drew his practice primarily from a middle-class neighborhood on the city's west side. For some unknown reason, the general practitioners in that area preferred to send their surgical patients to him. The reason why baffled me—and still does. At best, he was a so-so surgeon.

Dr. Weaver was already there when I reached the dressing room. He was at his locker, getting out of his clothes. He was in his middle fifties, skinny, and beginning to wrinkle, but with a pronounced paunch. When he took his clothes off, his dignity went with them. Until he got into uniform, he kept his eyes averted—like an ostrich, assuming that if he kept his head hidden he could not be seen.

I said good morning, and he murmured in reply, then I moved on to the lounge to see if there were anyone in there to say hello to. The lounge was at the far end of the dressing room. It had a couch and a number of chairs and a coffee table and a coffee machine—and a shower. It was a good place to wait—when waiting was necessary—and to catch a half hour's sleep—at those times when you were so dead tired that you could sleep anywhere. At the moment, it was vacant.

I did an about-face, went to the bins, got a uniform (green), then went to my locker, which was down a few yards and across from Weaver's locker. By then, he had on his green pants and gown. He was lighting a cigarette.

"Back, eh?" he said. His voice was a little like his body—skinny. "Have you met the new Head yet?"

"About an hour ago," I said, getting out of my clothes.

"We've got a little cocktail do coming up this evening," he said. By "we" he meant the attendings, the practicing M.D.s who were associated with Briggs. "How did he strike you?"

I shrugged. "Hard to tell," I said. "Everybody said a few words, and that was about it."

"Was Max Gar there?"

I nodded.

He dropped the subject. He rested his cigarette on the wooden bench that separated the two rows of lockers, then, standing in the narrow aisle, did a half-dozen knee-bends, then a half-dozen toe-touches. He was panting when he finished. He picked up the cigarette.

"I'm going to give these up and get myself a bicycle," he said.

19

"Is that better than knee-bends?"

"The cigarettes, I mean. I'm going to give up the cigarettes. Do you know how many muscles you use when you ride a bicycle?"

I shook my head.

"A hell of a lot," he said.

I had finished dressing. We left the lockers and went into the scrub room. From the containers over the sinks, we got caps and masks. Then, standing side by side at the sinks, we began to scrub, using stiff-bristled brushes and PhisoHex on our hands, digging in around the nails, between the fingers, over the knuckles, up the arms to the elbows.

"Little gook girl we've got this morning," Weaver said.

The girl was Korean, age twenty-three.

"Married an Army boy," he went on. "He brought her back over here. Quiet little thing. She's got a voice about like a bird. They're all right, I guess."

I didn't say anything.

When Weaver finished at the sinks, we went into the operating room. The circulating nurse handed him a towel and he dried his hands and arms. Next she held a gown for him. When he was in it, she powdered his hands. Then she held the gloves for him. He plunged his hands into them and was ready. I was next and she repeated the process.

The patient had arrived and was on the table. The anesthetist was in his place, checking his apparatus. The scrub nurse was rolling the instrument cart up to the table. The intern was standing by, bored. He had done the work-up, and that was where his function ended. Now, he could only watch.

The patient had been draped and prepped. The only part of her that was visible was the area over the kidney. From the work-up and Weaver's orders, I knew what had occurred prior to this moment, and what was to be done now.

The girl had gone to a GP complaining that over the previous several months she had been suffering severe headaches and nosebleeds. Examining her, he had found that she was acutely hypertensive, with a blood pressure of 240 over 160. He sent her to Briggs. X-rays showed that her right kidney was nearly 2 inches smaller than her left. The constriction of the main artery leading to the kidney was causing the organ to secrete renin, a substance that causes high blood pressure. Fortunately, the problem could be corrected by surgery. Our task was to widen the artery so that it would stop secreting renin.

Weaver went to the head of the table and looked into the patient's face. His own expression remained blank, so I assumed that, by then, the patient was unconscious.

"Pretty little girl," he said. "But when they get older, they get fat." He turned to me. "All right—you take it."

Weaver rarely performed an operation himself. Not because he wasn't competent. It was partly, I think, because he was lazy. But mostly it was because he realized that unless the residents got experience at the table they would never become surgeons. We appreciated this about him.

I stepped into place at the table, then looked at the anesthetist.

"Any time you're ready," he said.

Weaver spoke to the intern. "You get in there with him," he said.

The intern grinned—at least, his eyes seemed to smile—and stepped into the place across the table from

21

me. It was a break for him. He had expected to spend the time twiddling his thumbs.

I held out my hand. "Scalpel."

The scrub nurse slapped the instrument against my palm, and the operation began. I made the first incision, then went deeper. The intern began clamping off the bleeders.

I noticed that Weaver had moved away from the table. When I got the kidney exposed, I found that the X-rays had been right—there was indeed a narrowing of the renal artery. I severed it, completed the dilation, and set to stitching it back together. About an hour later, I finished the closing. By then, Dr. Weaver had left the operating room.

I had a half-hour before I was scheduled to scrub again. I went to the lounge. George Bruner and an intern, Mike Phelps, were there, also between scrubs. Bruner was stretched out on the couch, and Phelps was slumped in a chair. I dropped into a chair, too.

"Who did you have?" Bruner said.

"Weaver."

"Did he get that bicycle yet?"

I laughed. "Not yet. He still has to get past the first step—giving up cigarettes."

"What did you think of your new Head?" Phelps said.

I made a noncommittal face.

"I went up and shook hands with him," Bruner said. "He's got a firm grip."

"Did he look you straight in the eye?" Phelps smiled.

"Yeah, I think so."

"Then he's okay," Phelps grinned. "Any guy with a firm grip, and he looks you straight in the eye, he's loyal, reverent, trustworthy . . . uh . . . what the hell's the rest of that?"

"Gar seemed to be taking it all right," Bruner said.

"How could you tell?" Phelps said. "Gar's had the same expression since the day he was born."

"What did you think?" Bruner said to me. "You know Gar."

I made the noncommittal face again.

"Brandt made out okay," Bruner said. "After all the handshaking, he and Clover got into a conversation. I didn't catch any of it. I had to get out of there and scrub." He pushed himself up to a sitting position. "Listen, what are you and Sue doing on Sunday?" he said. "Anything?"

"Rest is about all," I replied. "We have two weeks to catch up on."

"You just had a vacation."

"That's what I mean."

"Marge and I thought we'd do the Museum of Science and Industry again," Bruner said. "Mostly for the kids. They like to run around and play hide-and-seek in the exhibits. You're welcome to come along."

"I'll see what Sue says. Thanks, anyway."

"Hell. We need somebody to help us find the kids."

Bruner and Phelps left. I scooched down further in my chair and thought about Brandt and Clover getting into a conversation. Brandt apparently had reached the same conclusion that I had—that the advantage had passed to him. And evidently, he was already starting to make time.

I wondered what I could do about it. I thought of somehow dissociating myself from Dr. Gar. But the idea turned my stomach slightly, so I discarded it. Finally, I decided that I had better show more interest in research. I would be faking—I just didn't have a natural inclination toward research—but the fellowship was important to me. Practicing a little hypocrisy, I decided, wouldn't hurt me. And it might help.

My next scrub was with Dr. Fred Ellender. I didn't look forward to it. Ellender was a bastard in the operating room. He was nervous and unsure of himself, and he took it out on everyone else, his assistant, his nurse, his intern, anyone who was near him.

Today, he began by castigating the patient, who wasn't even present. We were in the scrub room, at the sinks, when he started on her. "Goddamn fool," he said. "She's got no business being here. I told her five years ago she had a gall bladder condition. Dr. Hersey sent her to me and I told her then, goddamnit. I told her someday they'd be carrying her in here with her belly up. And, my God, what a belly."

The patient, a Mrs. Weimar, age forty, was so much overweight that it was ridiculous.

"Eats like a goddamn hog," Ellender said. "And laughs about it. Christ! *Laughs* about it! Can't make her mad. I told her. I said, lady, I'll tell you what your trouble is, you eat like a goddamn hog. Laugh! Jesus H. Christ!"

I heard a low sigh from the circulating nurse, who was standing by with the towels. She knew we were in for a bad time.

"Fat hog," Ellender grumbled. "I told her they'd carry her in here belly up."

Mrs. Weimar *had* been carried in. The night before she had gobbled down a double order of fried chicken and French fries, even though she had known about the gall bladder condition for years and had been warned about fried foods. About three hours later she had been hit by severe stomach pains and vomiting.

Her husband called Dr. Hersey, and he had sent an ambulance to get her and bring her into Briggs. The physical showed a tender right upper half of the abdomen. A tube was passed into her stomach and the food was sucked out. After that, Dr. Ellender was called in, and he decided to operate.

When we entered the operating room, the patient was groggy, but not yet under. Ellender went to the head of the table and spoke to her.

"I told you they'd carry you in here belly up," he snarled.

I heard a gurgle that may have been an attempt at a laugh.

Ellender stepped back from the table. "Knock her the hell out," he said to the anesthetist.

The patient was a mountain on the table. Draped in the sterile sheet, she rose in the middle like the top of Old Baldy.

Ellender spoke to the scrub nurse. "Let's have a little snap in it today," he said. "If you need sleep, go home and get it, don't get it here."

She kept her attention on the instruments.

Ellender glared at the intern. "I want you on the retractors," he said. "And goddamnit, you keep on your toes, understand? I don't want that goddamn flab flopping around in my face."

The intern nodded briskly.

Ellender faced back to the anesthetist. "Well?"

"Ready," he replied.

Ellender moved in to the table, and I stood across from him. The intern stationed himself at my side.

"Scalpel," Ellender muttered.

The scrub nurse pounded the instrument into his hand.

Very slowly, Ellender drew an imaginary line across

the right upper half of the abdomen. Then he took in a deep breath and released it as slowly and painfully as he had drawn the line. This was the ritual he performed before making an incision—as if he were hoping that if he delayed a half-minute someone would rush in and inform him that the building was on fire, relieving him, at least temporarily, of the responsibility of having to cut.

Finally, hesitantly, he made the incision. Perspiration popped out on his forehead. He poised the blade again—then suddenly backed away and threw the scalpel to the floor.

"Jesus H. Christ!"

That was the only explanation he gave. He held out his hand, and the scrub nurse slapped a fresh scalpel into it. Then Ellender stepped back to the table. And the circulating nurse swooped in and picked up the discarded instrument.

He cut deeper, down to the peritoneum—the thin sac that covers the intestine—then opened it. The gall bladder appeared, enlarged and fiery red.

By now the retractors had been attached, and the intern was tugging to keep the folds of fat out of the operating field. And I had been kept busy clamping off the bleeders.

"Put some muscle into that," Ellender snapped at the intern. "Keep that goddamn flab out of my face. My God, I might as well be doing this blindfolded, all I can see."

The intern tugged harder.

"Look at that son-of-a-bitch," Ellender said to me, indicating the gall bladder. "See that son-of-a-bitch?"

I said I saw it.

"Let's get the doo-hinkey in here," Ellender said to me.

He was referring to a needle and syringe.

The scrub nurse passed the syringe to me, and I slipped the needle into the gall bladder and began aspirating its contents. By clearing the gall bladder out, we hoped to prevent it from rupturing.

"You're draggin' ass again," Ellender barked at the intern.

In fact, the intern was doing as well as he could, considering the circumstances. Holding the retractors was a numbing, back-breaking job. All there was to do, literally, was hold on. His position, an awkward one, kept him from viewing the operation, which, if he had been able to, would at least have kept him from getting bored.

When I had finished, Ellender put out a hand and called for a clamp.

The scrub nurse passed him a ring clamp—which was what he needed.

Keeping his arm outstretched, and without even looking into his hand, he snarled, "Ring clamps, goddamnit, ring clamps."

The scrub nurse looked at me.

I rolled my eyes.

She lifted the ring clamp from Ellender's hand, held it for a moment, then dropped it back into his hand.

This time, he accepted it. "Goddamn dumb broad," he swore.

He placed the ring clamp at one end of the gall bladder, then called for another, and, when it was passed to him, fixed it at the other end of the sac-like organ.

Ellender straightened and uncramped his back muscles. He glared at the intern. "I've seen chocolate eclairs with more muscle than you've got," he grumbled.

27

Sensibly, the intern remained silent.

Ellender bent over the patient again. He called for a scalpel, received it—without complaint this time—then used the blunt edge to free the main artery leading to the gall bladder.

I set to work tying the artery with ligatures of 00 silk.

While I was at it, Ellender grumbled.

"If you broads stayed on your feet once in a while you'd have a little more snap in your butt," he said to the scrub nurse.

She laughed—thinly.

"Listen, when I'm doing a gall bladder and I call for a clamp, I want a ring clamp," he said.

"Yes, Doctor."

"I can't handle this whole goddamn thing alone. I need somebody in here who knows what I'm doing. Jesus! You know a ring clamp, don't you?"

She nodded.

"My God, I'd think you'd know enough to pass a man a ring clamp."

"Yes, Doctor."

He turned to the intern again. "You better tell 'em down there in the kitchen to stock up on some Wheaties for you."

"Yes, sir."

There was silence then, until I had finished.

Ellender took over again. He felt along the duct leading from the gall bladder, and along the common bile duct leading from the liver, searching for stones that might be blocking the passages.

"Clear as a bell," he said to me. He seemed disappointed.

Again, he moved away. I tied a ligature around the cystic duct to prevent the possibility of stones being pushed from the gall bladder into the common duct by way of the cystic.

While I did this, Ellender took up the chant again.

"What you want to do," he said to the scrub nurse, "is get your head nurse to show you what the goddamn hell a ring clamp looks like."

"I know what a ring clamp looks like, Doctor." Her voice was pinched and dry.

"By God, you'd never know it."

When I had finished, Ellender injected a saline solution between the covering of the gall bladder and the bladder itself. It was now quite easy to peel the gall bladder out of its bed and remove it. Ellender performed the task. Then he turned to his left to hand the bladder to the circulating nurse—who was standing at his right, ready.

"*Jeeeeee-zusssss!*" he screamed.

She hopped quickly to his left, took the bladder, and scurried away.

"Goddamn dumb broads!" Ellender howled.

The scrub nurse muttered.

"What?" Ellender snapped at her.

"Nothing, Doctor."

He gestured to me.

I interpreted—correctly, as it turned out—and, using 3-0 catgut, began closing the abdominal covering.

Ellender kept nagging at the intern. He asked him what state he came from. Ellender didn't like the state. He asked him where he had taken pre-med and med. Ellender didn't like the schools. He continued to ask questions and get answers. He didn't like anything.

When the covering was closed, I washed the wound with large amounts of saline. Ellender watched. He made no comment.

Then he said, "You close her up."

As I prepared to close the incision, he went to the head of the table.

"I told you they'd carry you in here belly up," he said to the unconscious Mrs. Weimar. Then he turned and strode from the operating room.

When he had gone, the post mortem on his technique began. He flunked.

I got to lunch about two that afternoon. After I had finished eating, I went to a lecture in the auditorium by an outside neurosurgeon. But I got called out in the middle of it to assist at an emergency appendectomy. It was late afternoon when we finished.

I took off for a half-hour and had a paper cup of miserable coffee in the lounge, then began making the rounds of the day's patients.

Mrs. Weimar was still in recovery. She was purring away, under sedative, like a contented Alp.

From Recovery, I went to the medical ward where the Korean girl had been taken. She was awake and smiling. Her blood pressure now was normal.

We talked for a moment. She was an attractive girl, with a round face and dark, sparkling eyes. Her voice was small, not much more than a whisper. Her name was Dolores McAlpin. I asked her about that. It didn't sound Korean to me. She explained that she had married an American soldier named McAlpin, and that her Korean first name didn't seem to fit with her husband's last name, so she had changed it to Dolores. Why Dolores? After, she explained, the movie star— Dolores Day.

On the way back from the ward, I saw Dr. Gar in the corridor. We stopped and talked for a moment. He asked me how I had enjoyed my vacation—but I realized that he didn't really care, he was simply asking to be polite. Which was understandable. I don't care whether other people enjoy their vacations or not, either. He mentioned that we were scheduled for surgery together the next day, then he moved on.

I went back to the lounge. Lou Manx and two interns were there. Manx was asleep on the couch, and the interns were playing gin rummy. I took over a chair and tried to dream up a research project. But I couldn't think very well with the gin rummy game going on. So I decided to go to the library.

On the way, I heard my name called on the public address system. I stopped at the first nurses' station and picked up the phone. The call was from Surgery. An accident case had come in. Dr. Link, a neurosurgeon, was on it, and he wanted me to scrub with him. I put off my research project—whatever it was—and ran for an elevator.

I got home to the apartment that night a little after nine. Sue had a tidbit for me. She had been talking to one of the interns' wives. Blabbermouth had told her about the cocktail party that was being held to introduce the attendings to Dr. Clover. And she had added that Paul Brandt had been invited to it—by Dr. Clover himself.

For dinner that evening, I ate Brandt's dust.

Three

THE FOLLOWING day began the same way the previous one had ended—with an accident patient. I was in the dressing room, getting ready for my first scheduled scrub, when I got a call to hop down to Emergency.

When I got there, the duty intern had a male, white, on the examining table. He was 60 and grizzle-faced. He had been hit by a truck. Almost all of his right ribs were fractured. He was a bluish color and gasping for breath.

"I can't get him out of it," the intern said.

The intern had done everything that logic would dictate. But, still, the old man seemed to be choking to death.

After examining him, I guessed that one of the ribs had punctured his right lung. The result was a flail chest—that is, instead of expanding, as it should, when the patient breathed, the lung was deflating.

For a moment, I didn't know what the hell to do. Then, suddenly, I remembered something I had learned in my freshman physiology course. I grabbed some Vaseline, smeared it on a bandage, then began wrapping the patient's chest as tightly as I could. The effect was almost immediate. The patient relaxed, his breathing became less labored.

"I don't get it," the intern said.

I explained that the tight wrapping had made the chest wall airtight, keeping the lung from deflating.

We finished the physical that the intern had begun. It came out negative except for the fractured ribs and the punctured lung. So I ordered the patient to be sent to the operating room, and I went up to scrub.

About a half-hour later, I had the patient on the table. I resewed the muscles and cleaned the wound, then strapped the ribs. The patient was sent off to Recovery.

The emergency had caused me to miss my first scheduled scrub, and I had a few minutes before the second one was due.

I went to the ward to check on my Korean girl. She was coming along nicely, her b.p. remaining normal. Then I dropped in on Mrs. Weimar, the gall bladder patient—all several hundred pounds of her.

She was a laugher, all right. I examined her dressings, and she hooted and howled all the way through it—though what was so hilarious about having a dressing examined eluded me.

By the time I finished, I was due to scrub again.

This time I was assisting Dr. Jerry Paulson. Paulson was a general practitioner—about the last g.p. left on the staff at Briggs. Several years earlier, he had been offered the choice of limiting himself to straight medicine—and being given the status of an internist—or continuing full-time with his operating room duties. But he got his hackles up, and insisted on going along as he was, handling everything. So the hospital didn't push it. Jerry was liked. His patients had confidence in him—he was always busy, always on the run—and when he got out of his depth, there had always been a sharp resident around to haul him out.

It wasn't right—he should have been kept out of Surgery—but that's the way it was.

This particular case appeared routine. The patient

was an 18-year-old female. The evening before, after dinner, she had complained of some right lower abdominal pain. Later, this was followed by nausea. Her mother had called Jerry Paulson. Paulson went to the house, examined her, and had her taken to Briggs. He had diagnosed the ailment as an acute appendix, and this morning we were to take it out.

I was at the sink, scrubbing, when Paulson came in. He was in his usual cheery mood, and, again as usual seemed in a hurry to get the whole business over with so he could get on to the next patient.

"I was at it 'til two this morning," he told me. "Old Mrs. Wilson. Pssst! Like that. Went out like a light. Couldn't get enough oxygen. Well, damn it to hell, she was eighty-seven. I say if you make it to eighty-seven you don't have much of a kick coming. You met Clover yet? Cocktail party last night. Couldn't make it. Me, not Clover. I suppose *he* was there."

He enjoyed a good laugh over that.

"Couldn't make it," he continued. "Measles case. Measles! My God, in this day and age. Bad case. The Larrup boy. I said to his mother—Mrs. Larrup—I said, we shouldn't have this here. Why didn't he get a measles shot? I said. She said she didn't know what I was talking about. My God, I said, in this day and age? Everybody knows about measles shots. So she said, well, why didn't you give him a measles shot? I said, My God, woman! Saw Max Gar. Guess he went to the cocktail party. I said, Max, my God! He made out like he didn't know what I was talking about. But that's Max. A man of two words."

We dried our hands, and the circulating nurse fitted Paulson, then me, into our gowns and gloves.

"Ever play contract bridge?" Paulson said to me as we walked toward the operating room. He didn't wait for an answer. "Took it up," he went on. "Relaxer. The missus said to me, Paul, what you need is a relaxer. Get me one of those chairs, I said. No, she said, Paul, what you need is a hobby. All right, I said, I'll get me some sixteen-year-old girlie."

We pushed through the swinging doors into the operating room. The patient, the anesthetist, the scrub nurse, and the intern were there.

"Got in a whole game the other night," Paulson said. "You play hands, and when you play enough hands, you've got yourself a game. Got something to do with scoring—haven't got to that part yet."

We reached the table.

"Well, we'd get into a hand—had the Browers over. Ted and Ellie Brower from across the street. Ted's in the steel business. First time he said that to me, I said, what do you steal, Ted? Been pals ever since. Well, we'd get into a hand, and the phone would jangle. Hop up. Peddle off. Ted said, Paul, I thought you doctors didn't make house calls any more. I said, Ted, I'll tell you, don't believe everything you read. Finally finished the game. Along about midnight. Ted said, Well, Paul, I'll say this, I never had a game like that before." He turned to the scrub nurse. "Hi, there, Betty, you look younger every day."

She smiled. "Good morning, Doctor."

He nodded to the intern. "Good to see you again."

The intern made ducking motions with his head, responding.

Paulson turned to the anesthetist. "How are we up there?"

"Ready, Doctor."

"Well, let's get this show on the road." He stepped up to the table—then backed away. "Hold it." He went to the head of the table, looking into the patient's face, said, "Yeah, it's okay—that's her," then moved back into place.

He asked for and received a scalpel, made the initial cut, then, going deeper, picked up the line of chatter.

"I said to the missus, well, hell, I can go to a cocktail party any time. I said, I'll tell you the truth, the farther away from cocktail parties I stay, the better. She said, well, but aren't you expected, though? I said—"

He interrupted himself, entering the abdominal cavity.

"Well now, look at that."

Red, swollen loops of bowel had emerged in the cavity.

"Going to have a time finding that appendix," he grumbled.

I wondered if this were some attempt at a joke. It was obvious that the patient's trouble was regional enteritis (inflammation of the bowel), not appendicitis. And enteritis was not something that should be handled surgically.

But Paulson wasn't joking. He probed in the cavity, trying to find the appendix. The operational field was so clouded by the diseased intestines that the appendix was completely obscured.

What to do? I didn't want to tell the damn fool that he was making a mistake. Yet I had to stop him.

"Could I close this one for you, Doctor?" I said.

He glanced up at me. "What? Sure."

"I'll close *now*," I said.

"What the hell's the matter with you?" His expression was no longer cheery. It was grim.

I lowered my voice as much as I could. "You've got an enteritis there," I said.

He kept probing. It was possible that he hadn't heard me.

I said it again, raising my tone a bit.

But he just kept digging for that appendix. His jaws were clenched tightly now. I guessed that I was getting treated to a show of the same stubborn streak that had made him refuse to limit his practice to either medicine or surgery.

Suddenly a spurt of blood shot up between us. It must have come close to hitting the ceiling.

I decided that if Paulson kept probing we were going to have a catastrophe.

I said it once more. Loud this time. "Doctor, you've got enteritis there, not appendicitis!"

He could have been deaf.

I left my side of the table, circled it, then when I reached his side, elbowed him out of the way. I didn't look at him. I just shoved. When he moved back, I stepped into his place.

I found the cause of the sudden spurt of blood. The vena cava had been nicked. I clamped it, then began suturing it.

The room was absolutely still. I didn't know where Paulson had gone, and I was too busy to look. But if he was still in the room, he was quiet for once.

When I had finished suturing the vena cava, I looked around. Paulson was a few steps behind me. He looked a little stunned, but not angry.

I moved back to my side of the table. Paulson returned to the place I had vacated. Without looking at me—or at anyone—and without a word, he began the closing. It went smoothly.

When he finished, he ordered the patient to be taken to Recovery. Then he said, not to anyone—more to the silence—"We've got a case of enteritis here. Case for Medicine."

He turned and left the room.

I stayed with the patient until she was wheeled out. When I left the operating room, Paulson had gone.

I went to the lounge. Tris Maney was complaining to a couple of interns about an emergency that had come in when he had been two minutes from getting off duty. It had happened a week earlier—and he was *still* griping about it. I tuned him out.

I wondered what to do about Paulson. Report what had happened? Or forget about it? The staff would know—the nurses and the intern would talk the first chance they got. But it would probably not go any further. If I kept quiet, it was unlikely that any action would be taken.

What was my duty—that was the question. I guessed I should report the episode. But what about Paulson? I thought about him. For years, he had been doing the best he knew how. And in most instances he had probably been doing the right thing. He was a dedicated man. Medicine was his life. Jumping up every time that goddamn telephone jangled. Running.

On the other hand, though, he had no business being in an operating room. Surgery had become too complex, and he hadn't kept up.

Maybe, after this, he would retire from surgery.

But I couldn't count on that. In fact I doubted that he would. He was too stubborn.

In the end, I decided to let it ride—to assume, and hope, that there would always be someone standing by who could take over if or when Paulson got stuck.

Now, looking back, I think I made the wrong decision. I was thinking more about Paulson than the patients. Nevertheless, that was the decision I made. And once made, it had to stick. From that moment on, it was too late to make a report.

I shared a table at lunch that day with Lou Manx and Paul Brandt.

Manx was in great form, hitting the groin with innocent questions.

"What is Clover *really* like?" he said to Brandt.

"I hardly got to talk to him," Brandt said. "The attendings had him cornered most of the evening."

"That should have given you a chance to make some time with Gar," Manx said. "Gar probably still has a lot of influence. Wouldn't you say?"

"Yeah . . . I suppose so," Brandt replied.

Manx turned to me. "What would you say?"

"Yeah . . . I suppose so," I answered.

Manx faced back to Brandt. "Now, it's your turn to ask me what I'd say," he said.

Brandt smiled. "Okay, what?"

"No comment."

"One thing, I don't think I did myself any good going to that blowout," Brandt said. "The attendings were a little icy. I guess they wondered what the hell I was doing there."

"What *were* you doing there?" Manx asked.

Brandt shrugged. "Who knows? When I went up to shake hands with Clover, I mentioned a paper he'd written—I had a question on it. He said it was a good question, and we'd talk about it. Then he invited me to the cocktail party, and said we could discuss it there. But we didn't. I couldn't get to him."

"You probably scared hell out of him," Manx said. "You probably hit on a flaw in his research, and he's trying to get on the good side of you to keep you quiet."

Brandt laughed. "Yeah."

Half looking at me, Manx said to Brandt, "How about Gar? Was he in the corner with Clover, too?"

Brandt squinted, thinking. "I don't remember," he said finally.

"Was he there?"

"Oh, yeah, he was there."

"You mean you saw him?"

"Sure I saw him."

"But you don't remember whether or not he was in the crowd around Clover?"

"He might have been. But I think I saw him with Dr. Frost most of the evening."

"What do you mean, *most* of the evening? I thought you couldn't remember."

Brandt laughed again. "Your spurs are cutting me," he said. "Get off my back."

Manx indicated me. "I was just asking for him," he said. "He likes to keep track of Gar."

"I don't keep track," I protested.

"Well, not any more, probably," Manx said. "What's the point to it—he isn't Head any longer."

"*When* did I keep track of him?" I challenged.

"If you weren't keeping track, why were you so interested in what he was doing at the cocktail party?"

"Who was—"

Manx was making a face at me—mocking me for protesting too much.

I shrugged and retreated. And Manx kindly switched the talk to a different subject.

I scrubbed with Dr. Gar on two cases that afternoon—one a spinal injury and the other a cancer case. The cancer patient was a woman in her middle thirties. She had four children. Her husband was a public relations man. He had read every article on cancer he could find. And he kept badgering Gar to try this and

40

that experiment—none of which were related in any way to the particulars of the case.

We opened the woman. But we were years too late, and all we could do was close her up again. If we had tried to cut, she would have died right there on the table. As it was, she would have a week, maybe two weeks more of life—such as it was. Gar sent her to the recovery room, with orders to pump her full of drugs and keep her that way.

Her husband was waiting for us when we got out of the operating room. Gar told him how it was. There wasn't any subtle way of saying it. The husband started to rave—he was going to sue Gar for malpractice. But then, right in the middle of the attack, he suddenly broke up and started sobbing. Gar sat him down—and motioned me away.

They sat there together for about a quarter of an hour—Gar talking, and the husband continuing to weep. I couldn't hear what was being said. But after a while the husband gave a kind of convulsive shudder, then hunched his shoulders and stopped crying.

When Gar left him, the husband continued to sit. But he looked stronger.

I wondered what words Gar had used. I knew that some day I would have to face such a situation myself. As we left the small reception area outside the operating room, I asked Gar what he had told the man.

He rubbed at his chin and answered, "Oh . . . you know."

That wasn't much help. I didn't know. But I didn't press him.

It was late by then, past the time when I was supposed to be off duty. But Dr. Gar hadn't dismissed me, so I followed along. We went to the medical section, then in and out of a couple of wards. Dr. Gar was making rounds, checking up on the progress of a number of his patients.

There were some surgeons who dismissed each case from their minds as soon as the patient was off the table. They had the next operation to worry about—period. But Dr. Gar liked to keep tabs. Lou Manx said he had a mother complex.

Our final stop in the wards was at the bed of a man named Cobbler. He looked to be in his forties. He had a strained, wincing expression. Dr. Gar talked to him for a few minutes—about nothing in particular, it seemed to me. Then we left and went to the small office behind the nurses' station on that floor. Gar picked a chart off the chart rack and handed it to me.

"What do you say?" he said.

I sat down in one of the chairs and looked over Henry Cobbler's history and physical. He was 46, and until about three months earlier he had been in excellent health. Then he began getting mild stomach pains right after eating. The pains became more severe, and he went to see a Dr. Hollander, a general practitioner. Hollander sent him to the Briggs clinic for a full check-up.

Cobbler was admitted into the clinic, where they sent him to X-ray and fluoroscoped him while he was swallowing barium, a thick whitish liquid. The X-rays showed a small ulcer in the stomach. It looked benign, but, just to make sure, they used a gastroscope on him. The scope is a large tube with a light on it. It is passed through the mouth, down into the stomach, where the light spots on the ulcer, allowing a clear visual inspection. This, too, showed that the ulcer was benign. But they still went a step further. A sample of gastric juice was taken and sent to the pathologist. Again the report came back that the ulcer was benign. At this point, Dr. Gar was called in to consult. Because somewhere along the line, someone still didn't trust all the tests.

"I think we've got an old maid in the clinic," I said. "If all this evidence doesn't mean anything, what does?"

"Feel," Gar said. "How do you feel about it? Are you sure?"

"It's right there," I said touching the chart.

Dr. Gar nodded. "Yes," he said, "it's pretty hard to argue with all that."

"Did I miss something?" I asked. I sensed that he didn't agree with the evidence.

He shook his head. "No, it's all right there, but I think I'll suggest that they wait it out a while."

He wrote his suggestion, recommending that Henry Cobbler be put on a rigid diet of milk and cream, and that he be kept in the hospital for at least three weeks.

"Maybe we'll get some movement by then," he said.

I didn't know what sort of "movement" he was expecting. But when I asked him, he was unable to explain. He was, I guessed, going by "feel."

We returned to our own floor then, and Dr. Gar went his way, and I went mine—home.

Sue had a jolly piece of news for me. She had gone shopping with Marge Bruner that afternoon, and Marge had suggested that she and I go along with the Bruners the next Sunday to the Museum of Science and Industry.

"I know," I said. "George mentioned it."

"Why didn't you warn me?"

"For what? Sunday is almost a week away."

"It's four days. And not about that—about the invitation, so I'd have an excuse when Marge mentioned it."

"What do you want with an excuse?" I said. "I could take the museum again."

"With the Bruner kids? That's like volunteering for the New York subway at the rush hour. Those kids are up and down the exhibits like monkeys."

"They're just kids."

"Monkeys."

So we decided to beg off, claiming we needed rest.

I went into the bedroom, where Peter, our two-year-old, was asleep. The room was a shambles. It looked as if it had been the scene of a riot.

"What happened in here?" I called out.

"Oh . . . Peter did that. He was fooling around."

I went back into the living room. "Peter was just fooling around, but the Bruner kids are monkeys?" I said.

She stared at me—hard. "Why do you always come home in a nasty mood?" she asked.

I could see where that would lead. So I did an about-face and went to the kitchen for a beer. While I was opening the can, I counted to ten. It helped. By the time I got back to the living room, I was ready to accept the premise that what the Bruner kids did was monkeying and what our kid did was fooling around.

Four

MY LITTLE Korean girl was having trouble again. It had been three days since she had been operated on. Since then, her blood pressure had settled to normal. Then, suddenly, in the early morning hours, it shot back up again, hitting 260 over 160.

At 2:00 a.m. I got a call from the medical resident. I got dressed and went back to the hospital. By the time I got there, he had pulled her b.p. down a bit. But it was obvious that she was still in trouble.

We stood in the corridor outside the ward on the medical floor and guessed at what might be causing the sudden rise in blood pressure. But guesses didn't help. The only thing to do was open her up again and find out.

I called Dr. Weaver first thing the next morning. When I told him what had happened, he agreed that she ought to go back to the operating room. He asked me to make the arrangements and said he would get right over.

About an hour later, we had her on the table once more. When we opened the abdomen, we found a large blood clot surrounding the entire right kidney. The clot was literally squeezing the life out of the kidney.

"Nothing we can do about that," Weaver said. "Out it comes."

He turned the surgery over to me, and I removed

the kidney. It was the best thing we could have done for her. With luck she could live a normal life with one kidney.

While I was still at the table, Dr. Clover came into the operating room. He had scrubbed and was evidently on his way to another room. He came over and stood watching.

Dr. Weaver told him why we were removing the kidney.

But Dr. Clover didn't seem much interested. Not that I could particularly fault him for that—we weren't exactly breaking new ground with a kidney removal.

"How does the other kidney look?" Dr. Clover said. "Will it handle the load?"

"Healthy," Dr. Weaver replied. "Good and healthy."

"The day will come," Dr. Clover said, "when that won't be a major consideration. Soon you surgeons will be able to take a bad pair of kidneys out and put a good pair in as easily as performing an appendectomy."

His reference to "you surgeons" bothered me. He was a surgeon too. But apparently he thought of himself more as the researcher who might develop transplants than the doctor who would perform the operation.

But then he said something that buoyed me up. He spoke to me by name—although I had never officially met him—and said, "Dr. Gar thinks quite highly of you. We had a talk about it the other evening."

There wasn't anything I could say to that. I nodded and kept my mouth shut.

"He tells me you intend to practice," Dr. Clover said.

"Yes, sir."

"That looks like the right decision," he said. I took the comment to be approval.

Dr. Clover remained for a few more minutes. He and Dr. Weaver discussed some details of administration. Then Dr. Clover left.

As I was on my way to lunch, a call came for me over the loudspeaker. Dr. Gar wanted me in one of the consultation rooms. When I got there, he was with another doctor, an internist. The internist, Dr. Parmalee, seemed to be in a scratchy mood. He was listening to Dr. Gar and making faces of disagreement.

Dr. Gar handed me a history to read.

It was on a male, age 49, named William Foster. I recognized the name. Foster was the executive vice president of an electronics firm. He was a "name" in the city. And he was on the Briggs board of trustees.

A routine chest X-ray taken by Foster's company had revealed a small spot on the right lower lobe of his lung. The spot hadn't been there a year earlier. His history, other than that, was fairly negative, except for the fact that he had smoked from one to two packs of cigarettes a day for something like twenty years. He had no cough, and he felt fine. There was a notation, however, that he had given up smoking about six weeks earlier. This is sometimes indicative of trouble, since a patient will often sense that something is wrong and subconsciously retreat from what his instinct tells him is the cause.

Dr. Parmalee was Foster's private physician. Foster had gone to him, and Parmalee had sent him to Briggs for a physical. Sputum was taken and examined for cancerous cells, and he was bronchoscoped (that is, a long tube was passed through his mouth and trachea into the bronchus of his right lower lobe). All the tests proved negative. At that point, Dr. Parmalee asked for a surgical consult, and Dr. Gar was brought in.

47

"I say the need is there," Dr. Gar was saying as I finished reading the history. "To me, the X-rays show it."

"Max—now don't take this personally—but sometimes I think you people are too anxious to cut," Parmalee said. "We've got a situation here. Bill Foster knows that his tests came out negative. He's feeling pretty good about it. Hell, I feel good about it myself. Now, if we tell him we want to cut, he's going to think we've got something to go on. And I can't tell him you've got a bug in your ear and you just want to go in there and look around. Let's remember who we're dealing with."

"A man with a spot on his lung," Dr. Gar replied.

"Don't give me that, Max. We're big boys. I say we've got to go at this cautiously. If I tell Bill Foster we want to cut, he's going to think there's something there. And, personally, I'm not convinced. Now, what are we going to tell him when he comes out of surgery and the report is the same—negative? What are we going to say—we were groping? Bill Foster is no goddamn fool. He's going to think, 'My God, they cut me open just to have something to do'. Let's face facts, Max. Bill Foster is not just some guy who walked in off the street."

"I don't care how he got here," Gar replied, "he's got a spot on his lung. And screw your goddamn tests, I say it's a spot that has to be seen. I have to get in there and look at it."

"All right, all right, how about this? Will you compromise with me? Let's give it a few weeks. Let's see what happens."

"If it's cancer, a few weeks could be too late," Gar said.

"Max, if it's nothing—if you go in there and find nothing, we're going to look pretty goddamn stupid."

"And if it's cancer, and we don't go in there and cut it out, in a few months Foster is going to look pretty goddamn dead," Gar said.

Parmalee sighed deeply. "Well, I'll tell you what I'm going to do," he said, "I'm going to straddle the fence on this one."

"What does that mean?" Gar said.

"Damned if I know."

Gar smiled—which, for him, was a laugh. "All right, I'll tell you what I'm going to do," he said. "I'm going to let the report read that I urged surgery. You're going to have to answer that, and I don't think you can do it and straddle the fence, too."

Parmalee threw up his hands. "Okay." He got to his feet. "You schedule him for surgery, but I think you ought to be the one to tell him what you're going to do—and why."

"I'll accept that," Gar said.

Parmalee left, shaking his head, muttering.

"Let me show you those X-rays," Gar said to me. "Then we'll go see our man."

We went to the X-ray lab, and Gar had the technician put the plates on the screen. The spot showed up pretty clearly. It was about one inch by one inch. I agreed with Gar—surgery was called for.

Next we went to the private room where they had put William Foster. He looked good—not at all like a cancer victim. He was a big man, muscular, with a square face and a thick head of reddish-brown hair. He was sitting up in bed, with piles of papers on his lap. A secretary—a trim, middle-aged woman—was seated in a chair, taking dictation.

Foster told the secretary to take a break and get a cup of coffee. She collected the papers, put them into an attaché case, and left.

Dr. Gar sat down in the chair the secretary had vacated. I stood near the end of the bed, feeling in the way.

"Mr. Foster, frankly, we've come up against a difference of opinion on this," Gar said. "As you know, all the tests show negative."

Foster smiled. "That didn't make me too unhappy," he said.

"No. But tests aren't always the last word. That spot is still in there. I don't like the looks of it. Dr. Parmalee is willing to ride with the tests. But I'm not. I recommend surgery. I want to go in there, and I want to look at that spot—up close."

Foster's smile faded. "You mean you think it's cancer."

"I don't know," Gar replied. "I'm not sure. And I want to *be* sure. I don't want to take a chance. The odds are that it *isn't* cancer. But . . ."

Foster nodded. "I see what you mean." He looked thoughtful. Then he said, "Suppose it is cancer. Will surgery help?"

"That depends. If there is a malignancy and it hasn't spread, then, yes, surgery could help. I could cut the spot out. But that's all pretty much conjecture—the spreading. The indications are, at this point, that it isn't cancer. I want you to understand that. My reason for wanting to operate is simply that the possibility of cancer exists. And I want to be sure—one way or the other."

"All right, that makes sense to me," Foster said.

Dr. Gar rose. "We'll have to have your permission to operate."

"Of course."

"Tomorrow morning," Dr. Gar said.

Foster nodded again, "Yes, let's get this over with."

We left the room. "Somebody underestimated the man," Dr. Gar said as we walked along the corridor. That was *all* he said about it.

After that, we stopped by to see Henry Cobbler, the man with the ulcer whom Dr. Gar had a "feel" about. He looked about the same to me. We stood for a few minutes, listening to him complain about his milk-and-cream diet. Then we headed back toward Surgery.

"The tests haven't changed," Gar said. "They still show that ulcer to be benign. I suppose Cobbler will be going home soon." But he didn't seem to be much in favor of the idea.

I finally got lunch about two that afternoon. Then I went to Recovery to see my Korean girl. She was doing well.

William Foster was the first case on the schedule the next morning. Dr. Gar and I were at the sinks, scrubbing, when Dr. Parmalee came in. He had been with Foster.

"Well, I don't know what you said to him," Parmalee said to Gar, "but I guess we're off the hook."

"I gave him my opinion," Gar replied.

"You can't depend on that," Parmalee said. "Your trouble is, Max, you don't have a feel for the nuances. You can tell a man the truth, and he'll clobber you with it. You just have to go slow, that's all. Feel your way along. You can stir up a lot of resentment, a lot of ill-feeling, with the truth. I saw this as a touchy situation."

As the circulating nurse fitted me into my gown and gloves, I heard Parmalee say, "Let's just hope to God we don't find anything in there. You find something, and you're going to put us all in one hell of a sticky situation."

"How's that?" Gar asked.

"It's going to make our testing procedures look pretty damn silly."

"Yes, I guess if we find something, we'll all be ruined," Gar said. "Maybe we better call the airport and have a plane standing by. We'll have to leave the country, won't we?"

"Max, for Christ's sake!"

I went into the operating room. The intern and the scrub nurse were there. And Foster was on the table, just barely conscious. At that moment, the anesthetist came in from an adjoining room. He took his place at the head of the table.

I spoke to Foster, and he smiled feebly. But I doubted that he had any awareness of what was going on.

Then Dr. Gar and Dr. Parmalee came in. Dr. Parmalee went to the head of the table and spoke to William Foster. He repeated a small operating room joke—which Foster, I'm sure, didn't hear—and had a good solitary laugh over it.

Then Dr. Gar stepped up to the table. He glanced around, as if to make sure that everyone was present, and spoke to the anesthetist. "Whenever you're ready."

A few minutes later, the patient was fully anesthetized.

At Dr. Gar's direction, the intern and I rolled Foster over to his left, so that his right side was up. Then we piled sandbags and pillows around him to support the position.

While this was being done, I could hear Dr. Parmalee muttering in the background.

The scrub nurse strapped a six-inch-wide strip of adhesive tape across the patient's hips, then we were ready to proceed.

Dr. Gar nodded to me—he was going to let me do the operation. I felt a great deal of elation. But it was quickly doused. Dr. Parmalee asked me to delay a moment—then he took Dr. Gar aside. I knew what they were discussing. Dr. Parmalee objected to my doing the surgery. And, since William Foster was his patient, I assumed that he would prevail. And I was right.

When they returned to the table, Dr. Gar took my place. He didn't say anything. And neither did Parmalee. But then, there was nothing that needed to be said. Foster was too important to Parmalee. He wanted Gar at the table. The fact that Gar had full confidence in me was not enough.

Dr. Gar made a large incision, starting at the spine and curving under the shoulder almost to the sternum. At the table, he was a graceful, casual man, and the incision appeared almost as if by magic, so deft was the action.

He stepped back then, and I resected (broke) the sixth rib, then inserted a rib-spreader. After that, Dr. Gar moved back into place and cut into the lung covering. The reddish, foaming lung immediately swelled into view. Next he dissected down to the hilum (the center of the lung) and the long, white, glistening phrenic nerve could be seen. This is the nerve that activates the diaphragm, causing it to expand and contract, a function essential to breathing. The heart, too, could be seen now, beating steadily.

Dr. Gar did some probing, looking for the spot on the lung. Then he found it. He motioned for me and Parmalee to crowd in.

The spot was small—at least, the core of it. But it was apparent that it had spread—how far, it could not be determined at that point.

"Jesus, God," Parmalee groaned.

53

"We better get a frozen section," Gar said.

Parmalee just nodded.

Gar backed away—moving Parmalee out of the way with him—and signaled to me. I moved into his place, then took a sample of tissue. I gave it to the nurse to take to Pathology.

The only thing we could do was wait. The pathologist would put the tissue on a slide for a quick screening test, then would give the intern a report to bring back to us.

Gar and Parmalee had moved to the side of the room. I joined them.

"The important thing right now is that this is handled right," Parmalee was saying.

"Why don't we wait for the frozen section?" Gar replied.

"What else can we do? But we have to look ahead. What are the consequences going to be, and how are we going to handle them?"

Gar shook his head. "I'm not going to cross any bridges. I want to see that report first."

Parmalee turned to me. "Nothing personal in that," he said.

I didn't know what he was talking about. I must have looked puzzled.

"At the table," he explained. "I'm sure you could have handled it. But Foster expected Dr. Gar to operate on him. And with the nurses and the intern present, somebody might have said something. You understand."

I said, yes, I understood.

Parmalee turned back to Gar. "Smoking," he said. "And he gave it up a few weeks ago. That's irony for you, isn't it?"

"We don't know what the report's going to be," Gar said.

"If I've given up smoking once, I've given it up a thousand times," Parmalee said. "It makes you stop and think."

"We don't have a report yet," Gar said. "And even if the report is positive, we're not going to be sure the cause was cigarettes."

"It sure as hell makes you stop and think," Parmalee insisted.

Gar went back to the table, and stood there looking at the exposed lung.

Parmalee was shifting from one foot to another. "What the hell's holding up that report?" he said after a while.

"It takes a half-hour or so," I said.

"Hell! It's been an *hour* now!"

In fact, it had been about fifteen minutes. But I felt the same way. Waiting for a path report, time is suspended. You feel as if you're floating around in space, helpless.

The patient in such an instance is fortunate in one way—he doesn't have to suffer the suspense. He's completely oblivious to the fact that somewhere a pathologist is going to say yes or no, and that, according to the yes or no, he may live or die. He's out of it. And, in that small way, lucky.

Gar came back. "It happens every time," he said. "Whenever I have to wait for a report like this, my head starts to itch."

"Get the nurse," Parmalee said.

Gar, of course, being sterile, couldn't scratch the itch himself.

"I'll give it a second," Gar said. "Sometimes it goes

away. I feel like a damn fool having a nurse scratch my damn head."

"I think we ought to think about the consequences," Parmalee said.

"What could happen?" Gar said. "She's scratched heads before."

"Max, I don't see the humor of that. You know damn well what I meant."

"Well, if a man is going to die, he's going to die," Gar said. "That's your consequences. I don't know anything you can do about it."

"This isn't—"

He broke off. The nurse had returned.

Parmalee hurried to her. They met, and she handed him a note. He looked at it, and his eyes told us what it said.

The report, of course, was positive. We had an anaplastic cancer on the table.

Gar didn't say anything. He went back to the table.

I followed, and Parmalee came after me.

Gar began probing again. He made room for me and Parmalee to crowd in beside him. The probing showed us how the cancer had spread. It was all through the area, in tiny bits. And there seemed to be no end to the spread. It would be impossible to remove.

Parmalee left the table after a while. He stood alone at one side of the room.

In time, Gar stopped probing. Probing was an act of futility. The cancer was everywhere.

"We'll close," he said.

About an hour later, we left the operating room—Gar, Parmalee and I. We shucked our operating clothes, then went to the lounge.

Parmalee dropped onto the couch, sighed, and lit up a cigarette. He inhaled deeply, then, suddenly pale, he snuffed the cigarette out in the ashtray.

"If you're waiting for me to say something—there isn't one damn thing I can do," Gar said. "You can try X-ray. But I don't have to tell you where that'll get you."

Parmalee shook his head, acknowledging that there was nothing that could be done.

"I just don't know what to tell him," he said.

"I think you underestimate him," Gar said. "Tell him the truth."

That suggestion seemed to horrify Parmalee. He shook his head again, rapidly this time. "The situation's just a bit too sticky for that," he said. "We've got some contradictions here."

"I told him what we might find," Gar said.

"Max, you're not the only one who talked to him, you know."

"Well . . . I talked to him last."

"Don't be so damn sure about that."

Gar looked a little more sour than usual. "He's your patient," he said. "That's all I can emphasize. What you tell him, that's up to you."

"The way I see it," Parmalee said, "for a man with that much cancer crawling around in him, he's in damn good condition. You saw that. Did he look to you like a man with cancer? Hell, no. But if I tell him the truth, we all know what's going to happen. He's going to fold. How long does he have? Six months?"

Gar shrugged, unwilling to commit himself.

"All right, let's say six months," Parmalee went on. "Six months, say, at the outside. Right now, he's feeling well enough. But if I tell him he's got a cancer,

57

he'll fold. He'll be miserable. In this case, I think I have a duty *not* to tell him."

"You're underestimating the man," Gar said again. "Not everyone is that afraid of death."

"Max, I have to use my own judgment."

Gar just nodded.

"I'll put him on X-ray," Parmalee said. "I'll tell him we want to clear up that spot."

"Then you want me to stay away from him, right?" Gar said.

"How do you mean that?"

"If I go near him, he's going to ask me. I can't tell him to talk to you about it. And I won't lie to him."

"You've done what you could, Max," Parmalee said. "I don't see any reason for you to have any further contact with him."

"All right. What if he asks for me?"

"I'll think of something."

"You can't put off the dying," Gar said. "In time, it's going to happen. Meanwhile, Foster is going to be telling everyone that the hospital gave him a clean bill. How are you going to explain that away?"

"Max, it's a matter of judgment. It's my opinion that Bill Foster will be served better by not knowing. You can question my technique, Max, but, damn, you can't question my judgment. It's what I think is right—and that's my prerogative, the prerogative of every doctor.

"All right," Max said. "But let me just say this: Your judgment, in this case, is not my judgment. I want you to know that. If, later, it gets messy, I want you to remember that."

Parmalee nodded agreement. "All right, Max. I'd say the same thing to you." He felt better, relieved. And he leaned back and got out his pack of cigarettes. "As a matter of fact," he said, lighting up, "that's an interesting subject—judgment."

Then we got a lecture. Parmalee's Law on Judgment. The gist of it was that what suited Parmalee was Judgment. What didn't suit him was Unethical—and damn close to being Communistic.

Five

WE WENT into the third month of our fifth year. The heat of the summer was fading. It was now pleasant to be out of doors. Everyone seemed to be in a better humor. But, personally, my morale had dropped a notch.

Dr. Clover had sliced Paul Brandt's operating room schedule almost in half, giving Brandt more time to work in the Research Building. This meant that the rest of us had to carry a slightly heavier operating load. But we didn't object, it was what we wanted, as much operating room experience as we could get. And since the arrangement also gave Brandt what he wanted— more time to do research—we all should have been pleased. That was the theory, anyway.

In fact, although I welcomed the extra time in the operating room, I was not happy about the arrangement. It was pretty obvious evidence to me that Dr. Clover had his eye on Paul Brandt. He hadn't rearranged the schedule to please the rest of us—that was simply a consequence. He had done it to accommodate Brandt. It meant—to me—that I had been left far behind in the competition for the fellowship.

I told Sue I was going to begin a research project.

"When?"

"As soon as I hit on something."

"No, I mean when are you going to find time for it? Your day is filled, you make the rounds of your patients every evening, and almost every night, you study. When are you going to work on research?"

"I'll have to fit it in," I said.

"You mean cut down on something else. What?"

"Maybe I can speed up my rounds," I said.

"But you always say that's your duty—even if you have to do it on your own time. You say it's your duty to follow up on your patients."

"I have a duty to myself, too," I said.

"Meaning what?"

"If Clover wants a research man, then, okay, I'll be a research man."

"You won't," she said. "You'll be an operating room man masquerading as a research man. You won't fool Clover, and, more important, you won't fool yourself."

"I can't let that fellowship go by default," I said.

"Well . . . I guess you'll just have to make up your mind how important it is to you. If it means that much . . . well, then you'll just have to do it."

At the time, I thought that was a hell of an unfair way of putting it. But it made me do some thinking about myself. And, the longer I thought, the longer I delayed beginning a research project.

Then I got some encouragement. An emergency case came in that Dr. Clover decided to handle himself. And he called on me—of all the fifth-year residents, including Brandt—to assist him.

The patient was a seven-year-old boy, Philip Meehan. He had been brought in from a small town in

Iowa by ambulance. The local doctor had diagnosed a ventricular septal defect—a hole between the two large compartments of the heart.

After I got the call from Dr. Clover, he briefed me, and we went to the private room where the boy had been put. His parents were with him. The boy was red-haired and freckle-faced and a bit on the frail side. His parents looked to be in their middle thirties. The mother was quite attractive—a redhead. The father was quiet and dignified.

Dr. Clover and I made a superficial examination. Then Dr. Clover made arrangements for the boy to be sent the next day to an operating room, where a cardiac catheterization could be done. Our own examination had indicated a loud pan-systolic murmur, that is, a murmur during contractions.

The next morning I went to the boy's room to wait for the stretcher to arrive so I could accompany him to the operating room.

"Can you say anything yet?" Mrs. Meehan asked.

"No," I replied. "Only what Dr. Clover said — we have to make a more thorough examination."

She turned to her son. "You watch now, Philip," she said. "It will be good experience." She faced back to me. "We want him to be a doctor," she explained.

"I want to be a mailman," the boy said.

Mr. and Mrs. Meehan laughed.

"He has an uncle who's a mailman," the father said.

"He's got security and he gets a pension," Philip explained to me.

"He doesn't even know what that means," his mother said. "He's just heard his uncle say it."

"And he gets a lot of fresh air," Philip said determinedly.

The Meehans laughed again.

The stretcher came. The orderly and I put Philip on it, then wheeled him away. The parents stayed behind.

When we got to the operating room, I called Dr. Clover. The cardiac catheterization was done, and it showed a large leak in the heart. The blood was going from the right ventricle to the left ventricle, not getting a chance to become oxygenated in the lungs. This resulted in unoxygenated blood being circulated to the oxygen-hungry tissues.

"Well, we're not in too bad shape," Clover said. "We're just lucky we caught him young. At this age, the mortality rate is something less than ten percent."

"Plastic graft?" I said.

He nodded. "First thing tomorrow. I'll put it on the schedule. Do you want to talk to the parents?"

I said I would.

I went back to the room. I told the Meehans what we had found, what we intended to do, and when we expected to operate.

Mr. Meehan asked how much danger there was.

I told him what Dr. Clover had said about the mortality rate.

"He's our only child," Mrs. Meehan said.

"We have a ninety percent chance for complete success," I said.

"What she means is, we can't have any more children," Mr. Meehan said. "We're pretty wrapped up in Philip."

All I could do was repeat what I had said before, that the odds were heavily weighted in favor of success.

I made arrangements for a room for the Meehans, then returned to the surgical floor.

I scrubbed that afternoon with Dr. Gar. The patient

was Henry Cobbler. Cobbler, on his milk-and-cream diet, had remained in a fairly static condition. X-rays had continued to be taken. His ulcer, the X-rays showed, was still there, but it was looking better.

Still, Dr. Gar did not "feel" right about it. Finally, he had recommended surgery.

No one else agreed.

But Dr. Gar was stubborn. He couldn't answer the others' arguments; he just kept saying surgery, surgery, surgery over and over again, like a broken record, and finally they all gave up — more out of exhaustion, I suppose, than because their minds had been changed.

So we put Henry Cobbler on the table that afternoon and opened him up. We had a number of observers — doctors who wanted to be there at the moment of truth to say "I told you so."

But they were robbed of the opportunity. The ulcer was malignant. We did a gastrectomy, taking the ulcer out entirely, then sent Henry Cobbler off to Recovery. Thanks to Dr. Gar's "feel" and stubbornness, Henry Cobbler had gained a few years of life that otherwise he would not have had.

Later that same afternoon, William Foster, the Briggs trustee, was brought back to the hospital. I saw him being taken to Radiation Therapy on a stretcher. Now he looked like a fatally sick patient. He was drawn and colorless, a fuzzy reflection of the man he had been.

Dr. Parmalee was walking beside the stretcher, grim and silent.

I spent some time asking myself who had been right — Gar or Parmalee? Parmalee's motive for not telling Foster the truth, I suspected, was self-interest. But the fact that his motive was wrong — if it was —

did not necessarily make his decision wrong. What would be gained by telling Foster that he was going to die? The way Parmalee had handled it, Foster had had a few weeks of life that were not clouded by the awareness of coming death. If he had been told, he could not have enjoyed those weeks.

On the other hand, withholding the truth was a form of lie. And no matter what the consequence, I could not completely convince myself that a doctor had any right to lie.

Still, I wasn't sure what I would have done. I remembered that in not reporting on Dr. Paulson's blunder I had withheld the truth — or, to put it another way, told a lie. And I had persuaded myself that I was doing the right thing.

The only conclusion I reached was that I was not qualified to throw stones at Dr. Parmalee.

I got to the hospital early the next morning and went to see Philip Meehan. His parents were there, and his nurse — on orders — was giving him an anesthetic. The boy looked paler than before, but it was from fear; his condition had not worsened.

I talked to Mrs. Meehan for a few minutes — Mr. Meehan was sitting by the bed, holding his son's hand — and reassured her as much as I could, repeating the fact that the odds were in favor of success. Then I went to scrub.

Dr. Clover was already at the sink.

"Have you been up to see the patient?" he asked.

"Yes, sir."

He didn't say whether he had been there or not. But the Meehans hadn't mentioned it. If he hadn't been, I wondered why not. Actually, it was *his* duty, not mine. But there are surgeons who think of patients as simply patients, and no more. I supposed it was possible that Dr. Clover was one of them.

When we were scrubbed and gowned we went into the operating room. Philip Meehan was just arriving. The drug had taken effect and he was almost unconscious.

He was draped with the sterile sheet. And while this was being done the anesthetist came in and took his place at the head of the table and began inspecting his various mechanisms.

Dr. Clover moved about, speaking to the scrub nurse, the intern, then falling into conversation with the anesthetist.

I stood near the table, glancing from the by-pass machine, a Rube-Goldberg-like apparatus that was to be used in the operation, to the face of the boy. His cheeks had regained some of their lost color, as, in unconsciousness, he had relaxed.

The scrub nurse prepped the operational area. Then Dr. Clover took his place at the table, and I moved to the other side. Finally, Dr. Clover nodded to the anesthetist.

A few seconds later, the anesthetist said, "Ready."

Dr. Clover made the first incision and I began clamping the bleeders. When he reached the heart, he called for the by-pass. Using catheters, I hooked both of the main veins of the heart to the collecting tubes of the by-pass, tying the veins so that no blood could escape. Then I connected the femoral artery to the pumping side. Now the by-pass could take the place of the heart, pumping blood and oxygenating it during the surgery.

Dr. Clover placed a tube in the left ventricle, or chamber, to draw off blood, so that he would have a dry surgical field. Then he made a crosswise incision in

65

the right chamber. This incision paralleled the course of the right coronary artery. If this artery had been accidentally cut, muscle tissue would have been destroyed. But there was no hesitation in Dr. Clover's movements. I felt — as I had months earlier when I had first seen him — that he had total confidence in himself.

We could now see the hole in the heart. Dr. Clover straightened, and motioned the intern and me to get in close and have a good look for ourselves. We bent over and peered at the defect for quite a while. It was fascinating. Then he motioned us back and began the repair, fitting a patch of finely knitted Dacron cloth over the hole and sewing it in place with 3-0 black silk suture.

It was delicate work, and the minutes dragged, as stitch by stitch by stitch Dr. Clover proceeded. I kept check on the by-pass machine. Meanwhile, I thought about the research that had made this moment possible. Someone — someone like Paul Brandt — had put in — how many hours? — trying and failing until this technique was perfected. As a result, Philip Meehan had an excellent chance of living a normal life. It was something to think about.

When the hole in the heart was closed, Clover sewed up the incision in the chamber, again using 3-0 black silk. After that, I removed the aortic clamp, hoping to eliminate air from the chamber. Next, the by-pass was disconnected, and the wound was closed.

Philip Meehan was moved to a stretcher, which was adjusted to a head-down position. The purpose of this was to lessen the chance of cerebral air embolism — an air bubble in the brain.

As soon as the patient was headed toward Recovery,

Dr. Clover left the operating room. He made no comment on what had occurred.

Myself, I had a strange let-down feeling. The operation had gone well. Perfectly. Perhaps too perfectly —if that is possible. Standing at the table, I had had the feeling that we were all machines—Dr. Clover, the intern, the scrub nurse, me — similar in nature to the by-pass. We were there, functioning as we had been built to function, doing a job, and doing it well, but without any other motive than to get it done.

I had never felt that way with any of the other surgeons — not even the worst of them. They had all seemed to recognize both their own and the patient's humanness. With Dr. Gar in particular there was never any doubt that he knew that he was a human being — fallible — tending to another human being — vulnerable.

This was not to say that Dr. Clover was a lesser surgeon. Dr. Gar could not have performed the operation better. But, to me, it was a disappointment. An element — spiritual, perhaps, although I am not comfortable with that word — was missing.

I had a call for a consult when I left the operating room.

I went to the medical floor and looked up the resident, Dan Hickey, who had summoned me. He had a female, white, age sixty-three, with an abscess on her right hip. It was obvious that it had to be drained. But, to do that, I had to get her permission to operate.

The trouble was that the woman and I had a bit of difficulty in communicating. She was of Slavic stock, and although she had been in the U.S. for a number of years, she had not learned the language as well as she might have.

I showed her the form, read it to her, explained in

my own words what I had just read, then asked her to sign it.

She shook her head. "No, *Muz*, no."

"It is necessary," I said. "Must. Yes."

"*Muz*, no!"

(At the time, I thought 'Muz' was a corruption of 'Must' — that, to my 'Must. Yes.' she was replying 'Must. No.' Later I learned from a friend of Slavic extraction that '*Muz*' was, in her language, the word for 'husband', and that she was trying to tell me that her husband had told her not to sign anything.)

We kept that up for a while, I insisting, and she replying, "*Muz*, no."

Finally, I left the room and went down the corridor to the small reception room to try to figure out a way to get her permission. Nothing suggested itself, so, I returned to the surgical floor, deciding to let the matter rest for a while. Lou Manx was in the lounge. I told him my trouble.

He reached for the release form. "I'll get it for you," he said.

I gave him the form, and he left.

While he was gone, I went to Recovery and looked in on Philip Meehan. He was still under the influence of the anesthetic. Then I went up to his room. It occurred to me that Dr. Clover might not have gone to see his parents after he had left the operating room. But he had. He had told the Meehans that the operation had gone well, and that they would be able to see their son as soon as he was ready to leave Recovery. They seemed to be bearing up fairly well, although I could see that Mrs. Meehan had been crying.

When I got back to the lounge, Lou Manx had returned. He handed me the release form. The woman's signature was on it.

"How the hell?" I said.

"I told her if she wouldn't sign the form then she'd have to sign a paper to that effect, releasing us from responsibility," he said. "She saw my point and I gave her the form and she signed it."

"How did you get all that through to her?"

"The game," he said.

"The what?"

"Charades. I acted it out for her."

I took him at his word, but later, thinking about it, I began to doubt. How would he act out "responsibility"? I suspect he was kidding me and I was too dumb to get it.

Anyway, in possession of the release form — ethically acquired or not — I ordered the woman to be moved to one of the small operating rooms.

When I got there, she was on the table, and a nurse was fluttering around her. I injected procaine, a local anesthetic, then, using a scalpel, nicked the collection of pus. It oozed out, yellow and thick and mixed with blood. I put a drain on it and left the patient in the care of the nurse, after telling her that she could go home in a few hours and come back for a follow-up appointment in three days.

It was late afternoon by then. I went back to Recovery to check again on Philip Meehan. Now, he was beginning to come out of the anesthetic. He hadn't opened his eyes yet, but his mouth was moving, and his tongue was licking at his lips, a reaction to dryness. The signs looked good.

I stood by his bedside a few minutes. The Recovery room had always fascinated me. It was like another world, sufficient unto itself — unique.

There were twelve beds, and for some reason that was completely hidden from me, the prettiest nurses were always on duty. This had always seemed somewhat of a waste, since most of the patients were unconscious. But, then, everything in the recovery room was particularly "right" — so the pretty nurses probably did make some sort of sense; they were merely an extension of the "rightness."

Everything — the furniture, the paint on the walls, the equipment — appeared to be fresh and new. Above each bed was an outlet where oxygen could be hooked up. Beside each bed was a small table with special equipment for each patient, according to the patient's needs. And beside the table was a small, transistorized box that could be used to monitor the patient's blood pressure, pulse, and cardiogram. A warning buzzer sounded if the blood pressure fell below a certain level or if the pulse went above or below a specific setting.

And over all this hung a blanket of almost total silence. The nurses moved like ghosts, touching each piece of equipment with extreme care, so that there was no sound of contact, no click, no scraping.

When I left the recovery room, I went to check out, but on the way, I stopped. I had the feeling that I was leaving too soon — the feeling of something left undone, or, more accurately, the feeling that if I left I might miss something. There was no basis for the sensation, but whatever it was, it was strong enough to keep me at the hospital. I called Sue and told her I was tied up — which was not the truth, actually — and that I would eat at the hospital. I told her I couldn't be sure when I would be home. She accepted the circumstance gracefully — or resignedly — having become used to it.

Then I went down to the cafeteria to see what the cooks had managed to spoil.

Six

I HAD WAITED through the line in the cafeteria, finally got my food, and was sitting down at a table occupied by two second-year residents when my name came squawking out of the loudspeaker. Normally, I would have said something uncomplimentary about public address systems. But, this time, I was expecting "something," and this, I guessed, was it.

I left my tray on the table and went to the phone. The call was from Recovery. Philip Meehan had regained consciousness and had immediately gone into a deep coma. I slammed the phone down and ran from the cafeteria.

When I got to Recovery, a medical resident and an intern were working over the boy. But I could see—and they knew — that nothing substantial could be done. His mouth drooped open, the muscles of his face were slack. It looked as if a pocket of air had remained in his heart chamber, and had now escaped and gone to the brain. And what moments before had been a bright seven-year-old was now in all likelihood an imbecile, who barring a miracle, would either die or live as a vegetable.

There was nothing I could do in Recovery except get in the way of the medical resident, so I left. Dr. Clover had been called, and he came hurrying up just as I stepped into the corridor. I told him what we thought had happened, and he hurried on into the room.

I walked slowly down the corridor to the small waiting room. It was vacant. I slumped down in one of the chairs and sat staring blankly into space. I felt more inadequate than I had ever felt before. There was nothing I nor anyone could do. And there was nothing that could have been done before. It was one of those tragedies that are beyond prevention. We had done everything right, but nature had gone against us.

I couldn't keep remembering Philip Meehan as I had seen him before, when his face had still been expressive, bright-eyed. It would never be that way again. He would never be a boy again, he would never grow up to be a man. That bubble of air in his brain had turned him into an organism. He would have to be fed, bathed, carried. Until, finally, he died. And the end would not be long in coming.

I thought of my own happy childhood. For some reason, I remembered the winters, in the park, ice skating on the pond. I remembered my hands freezing in my wet gloves, and my face raw with cold. Recalling it should have been unpleasant. But it wasn't. Because the cold and wet was distant. What was real was the joy. The great fun of skimming over the ice. I could hear the shouts of the other children, and my own shouts — meant to be loud, but muffled by the cold air.

Then I cried, knowing that Philip Meehan would never have this. Not this, not any of the joys of his age. Nor any of the pains. He would have nothing. Simply and plainly nothing.

Dr. Clover came in and I got up and went to the window and stood with my back to him, embarrassed that I had been crying. I heard him sit down. There was silence for a long time.

Then he spoke. "It's always worse this way . . . a

child, but there was nothing we could have done to prevent it. We did all we could. You realize that, of course."

"Yes," I said.

"Then we have nothing more to say to ourselves. Brooding won't help anyone. This thing has happened, and that's it. It isn't the first time, it isn't the last time. Now, we have to do what has to be done next. We have to put this thing away, put it behind us, and go on."

I nodded.

"The Meehans have to be told," he said. "I think it would be a good idea for you to do it."

I turned and looked at him — a little dumbly, I suppose. It was *his* responsibility to tell the Meehans.

"That isn't an order," he said. "It's a suggestion. I'm aware that it's my job. But in there in the operating room, all of the functions that were performed, they were my job, too. However — in there — I allocated some of those duties to you. The purpose was so that you could learn by doing, to help you become a surgeon, a doctor. All right, now there is a further duty. The responsibility doesn't necessarily end at the operating room door. And I'm offering you the opportunity to perform that duty for me. It's part of the whole."

I nodded again, understanding now.

He got to his feet and glanced at his watch. "Good night, Doctor," he said. Then he left.

I stood for a moment, delaying, a little afraid. Then I went back to Recovery. The medical resident and the intern were still with the boy, but their efforts had had no effect. I got the official decision from the resident, then left Recovery and headed for the room where the parents were waiting.

When I entered the room, the Meehans apparently

saw in my face that I had bad news. They didn't ask me anything, they waited for me to tell them. The first words were the hardest to find. There didn't seem to be any right way to begin. But somehow I got it out. Then, after I had said what had to be said, I began giving them the technical details of what had happened. Not because I thought they wanted to know or that they would be comforted, but only because, having said what had to be said, I simply could not stop talking. I was afraid of the silence that would follow.

They were stunned at first. There was a moment of disbelief, then the shock of realization. The father seemed to age several years in the span of a second. His face became drawn and gray, his eyes dulled. The mother, on the other hand, didn't seem to change a bit. She just stared at me, transfixed.

Then I suddenly realized that they weren't really listening to what I was saying. And I stopped talking. It was as if I had given a signal. Mrs. Meehan covered her face with her hands, and, behind them, sobbed softly. Mr. Meehan put an arm around her.

I told them I would come back later; then I left the room. I walked down the corridor to the nurses' station. The duty nurse was a middle-aged woman. She asked me what had happened, and I told her.

"You shouldn't leave them alone," she said. And she left the desk and hurried down the corridor toward the room.

I stayed at the desk, in a kind of trance. About ten minutes later, the nurse came back.

"I told them to go and get a bite to eat," she said. "But they want to wait for him." She shook her head disapprovingly. "They ought to go somewhere, get out of here, and talk it out. Then they could come back."

"Do they need anything?" I said.

She shook her head.

I went back to Recovery. The resident was just coming out. He said he would take over, that there was no reason for me to stay. And he was right, the boy was his responsibility now.

But it was difficult to let go. I thought about going back to see the Meehans again. But I didn't — because still I didn't have anything to say.

Again, I simply stood for a moment, detached, without purpose. I didn't know where to go. I didn't want to go home. Sue would see that something had happened, and she would ask me what, and I would have to tell her. I didn't want to talk about it.

So after a time, I went back to the surgical floor, and then to the lounge. There was no one there. I got a paper cup of coffee and sat down. I thought about Dr. Clover. How he had been able to say good night and go home. It wasn't, I was sure, that he hadn't been affected. But he had been able to take it in stride; acknowledge that a tragedy had occurred and then proceed.

What was his secret? How did he do it?

I wanted to know. It seemed necessary to find out. Because I realized that, as he had said, this would happen again. There would be other Philip Meehans. Probably an unending chain of Philip Meehans. I would have to get used to them.

But his secret, whatever it was, eluded me. I could only hope that time would eventually whisper the answer.

When I finished my coffee, I left the lounge and went to the duty room, where I found the second-year surgical resident who was on call. I told him I would take his shift. He looked at me as if he thought

I had lost my mind, and he waited around a moment, expecting an explanation. But I didn't give one.

Fortunately for me, it was a busy night. About an hour after I had taken over the duty, I got a call from Emergency. When I got there, the intern had a seventeen-year-old boy on the examining table. The boy had been brought in by his mother — who was standing by, wringing her hands — complaining of abdominal pain and vomiting. The boy looked as if he had just finished a mile run; he was panting and pale and sweating. The intern had found a tenderness in the lower abdomen. I touched it, and the boy winced. When I took my hand away, the boy screamed.

"Get him up to Surgery," I told the intern. Then I went to the scrub room.

It was obviously appendicitis — and apparently in an acute stage.

While I was scrubbing, a nurse came running in. The boy had lost consciousness on the way up to the operating room, she told me. She suspected that the appendix had burst.

The boy and I and an anesthetist reached the operating room at the same time. While the anesthetist was fiddling with his instruments, the orderly lifted the boy on the table. As soon as he had been intubated, I made my incision.

The appendix *had* burst. It was a messy job. But about an hour after the boy had been rolled onto the table, he was out of shock. I closed him and sent him to Recovery.

I went back to the duty room and collapsed on the cot. My legs were aching. I had been standing at the table too long for one day.

But just when I was on the edge of sleep, another call came from Emergency.

It was another boy. An eighteen-year-old Puerto Rican, this time. He had been dragged in by a couple of cops, holding onto his chest. When I took his hand away, a spurt of blood shot out.

I told the intern to get the kid up to the operating room, then I called a cardiac resident, Phil Eilers. He listened to me, grumbled, and said he was on his way.

I hurried up to the scrub room. I was finishing my scrub when Eilers came in.

"This better be my baby," he said, "or I'll haunt you from this day on. I just got into the sack when you called."

He started scrubbing, and I went into the operating room.

The boy was on the table. A nurse was at the anesthetist's position. I told her to put him out.

A minute or so later, she told me he was ready.

The duty intern hadn't appeared yet, but I didn't want to wait. I started cutting and clamping, cutting and clamping.

I was down to where I could see the heart when the intern and Eilers came in. Eilers took over. The knife had penetrated the heart, and he began the slow, delicate process of repairing the wound. Meanwhile, I sat on a stool in a corner and waited. My eyes were drooping. Finally I fell asleep — sitting up.

The next thing I knew, the intern was shaking me.

I went back to the table. Eilers had finished and was ready for me to close. But, after one look at me, he said, "For Christ's sake, go hit the sack," and proceeded with the closing himself.

I went back to the duty room, fell on the cot, and slept soundly until the alarm awakened me at seven.

I felt much better about everything the next morning. The night's work had helped. I had somehow worked Philip Meehan out of my system. Not entirely, of course, but enough to let me function normally again. And I decided that perhaps that was at least part of Dr. Clover's secret — just going on. In spite of what you might feel, going on.

The Meehans, when I saw them a little later, looked worse than they had the night before. Now, the mother's face had aged too. They told me that the medical resident had suggested that they put the boy in a chronic home. And they were considering it. Although they had not yet made a decision.

I told them I agreed. Philip wasn't the seven-year-old boy they had brought to the hospital. That boy was dead. He had died in Recovery. What was left was a few partially functioning organs inside the skin of Philip Meehan. There was nothing they could do for him. He would be better off, in fact, in a place where his condition could be cared for medically — until finally even what was left died.

I think my telling them that helped a bit. They knew apparently that parting from him was the only way, but still there was the feeling that in doing so they would be disloyal to him. They wanted someone else — some disinterested third party — to tell them no, they would not be disloyal, they would not be cruel, they would be acting in the child's best interests.

They hadn't yet made the decision when I left them, but they were closer to it.

I called Sue then. I told her there had been a number of emergencies, and that when I had finished I had been too tired to cross the street to the apartment building. She didn't believe me — not entirely — but she didn't pursue the subject, which I appreciated.

At lunch that day, I sat with Lou Manx and Tris Maney.

Maney was complaining about his sister. She had announced her engagement to a book salesman, and he didn't know what the hell good a book salesman was ever going to do him. The world was closing in again on its victim.

"He may not be healthy," Lou said. "For all you know, he may need everything taken out. He could become your best patient, the making of your career."

"He sounds healthy to me," Maney said. "Her letter says he's six feet two."

"There's a diagnosis for you," Lou said to me. "He's six feet two, so he's the picture of health." He faced back to Maney. "Stout heart," he said. "Maybe your sister was lying. All women lie about their men. Maybe he's only five feet nine. That's a thousand-dollar ulcer operation right there. Be of good cheer."

"She never has liked me," Maney said, ignoring Manx's comment and getting back to his sister. "She was going with a guy at IBM before. A guy with a future. The trouble was, she could never stand me. Why? Damned if I know. I gave her every break in the goddamn world. I used to go out of my way to talk to her. You know. I'd come into the house, and there she'd be, and I'd sit down and try to talk to her. And five minutes later, she'd hop up and take off. For some reason, she's just never liked me."

"She's probably a great judge of people," Manx said.

It missed Maney by a mile. "I wouldn't say that," he replied. "She's pretty common-everyday. She didn't even go to college. My father wanted her to, but my mother said, what the hell for? And, anyway, my sister didn't care much for the idea. She went to business school, then got a job in an office. I used to say to her, who are you going to meet in some office? And see what happened? A book salesman."

"I guess you were just born under a black cloud," Manx sympathized.

"Boy, you said it."

Maney left the table then. And a few minutes later Paul Brandt came over.

"Put any dogs to sleep lately?" Manx said to him.

I guessed that in some way dogs were involved in Brandt's research project.

"A whole pack just this morning," Brandt smiled. "Didn't you hear the howls?"

"I thought that was Maney when he got that letter from his sister," Manx said.

Then he had to explain to Brandt what he had meant by the reference to Maney's letter. After that, he said, "Don't you feel a little like a murderer, cutting up all those innocent dogs?"

"I'm not cutting up any dogs," Brandt said. "I haven't lost a dog yet."

"What exactly are you doing?" I asked.

"I'm trying different plastics to try to work out an artificial heart valve," he said.

"You mean to do transplants?" Manx asked.

Brandt nodded. "I have an idea that the trouble may be in the plastic. So far, the blood keeps clotting around the valve. Which, of course, is no good."

"Where are you getting all that plastic?" Manx asked.

"I'm working with one of the instrument manufacturers. They're making up the valves, and I'm doing the research."

"Is Clover in on it?" Manx said.

"He's helped," Brandt replied.

"How many valves have you tried?" I asked.

He thought for a minute, then shrugged. "Damned if I know. I have a record, but I can't remember off-hand."

"You know, you may be off on the wrong track altogether," Manx said.

"That's right, that's possible," Brandt replied. "It's hit-or-miss, but I have to keep at it until I find out, one way or the other."

"Suppose it isn't the plastic," I said. "There's all that time — phlooey."

"Nooooo . . . not exactly," he said. "I'll have eliminated one possibility. So it isn't a waste."

"Just how the hell many possibilities are there?" Manx asked.

Brandt shrugged. "Hundreds. I haven't even got a start on all of them yet."

"You mean this could run on for years?"

"For years and years and years," Brandt said. "And then it could end up with nothing."

Manx looked at him painfully. "You know what your trouble is," he said. "You need to meet a nice girl."

Brandt laughed. "I met a nice girl once. No fun."

"You're right," Manx said. "What you need is a bad girl. And who knows more bad girls than anybody? Me. I'll fix you up."

"Yeah, okay, I could use a night off," Brandt said. "You do that."

"In fact," Manx said, getting up, "I'll do something about it right now. I'll let you know," he said, leaving the table.

When Manx had gone, I told Brandt about Philip Meehan — that it, about the case, not how I felt about it. "Is anything being done about that — air emboli to the brain?" I asked.

"Somewhere, by somebody, I suppose," he replied.

"I don't know about all the research that's going on. But, as I say, probably, by somebody, somewhere."

"But you don't know of anything?"

He shook his head.

"I've never cared much for research," I said. "It's standing at the table that gets me. I feel like I'm doing something, right there, and I know how it's going to come out. Or, at least, I'll find out soon. But, research, you never know. Like you said, you may have to go on and on and on for years, and even then, there's no guarantee that you'll have anything."

He shrugged again. "It's what I like," he said.

"You don't mind? The uncertainty?"

"No. I don't think of it that way. I just take it step by step. I try a thing, and foul out most of the time, then try something else. I don't really think much about when I'm going to get wherever I'm going. Or *if* I'm going to get there even. If I thought about it, I'd probably chuck the whole goddamn business. I start a step, and finish it, then start the next step. That's the way I see it — not as a project, as steps."

"How much time do you give it?" I asked.

"All the free time I have. Which is a good deal. Clover has jiggled my schedule so I can spend more time at it than I would normally be able to. And, I usually give it two or three nights a week, and sometimes the weekend. It depends a lot on what else comes up."

Manx come back to the table. "You're fixed," he said to Brandt. He sat down. "This is her address," he said, giving Brandt a slip of paper. "It's on the north side. She's a blonde, and what more need I say?"

Brandt looked at the address. "I know where that is," he said.

"Just one thing," Manx said. "If she mentions something about your father being a movie producer, tell her you don't want to talk about it. She'll understand. I told her you two don't get along too well."

Brandt grinned. "That's okay," he said, "I don't mind talking about it."

"Just don't talk *too much* about it and get caught," Manx said. "I want to keep my welcome there."

"Okay, I'll talk about *your* father, the movie producer," Brandt said. "Or is that what he is?"

"Don't be corny," Manx said. "My father is a Broadway producer. This kid is an artist — art for art's sake. She's only interested in you, son of a movie producer, as an ace in the hole. My old man may not have a part for her in his next play. He may do something with an all-male cast."

"Am I supposed to remember all this?" Brandt said. "If I am, forget it. It's not worth it."

Manx grinned. "I'll see you tomorrow," he said. "If you can still say it's not worth it, I'll know what you *really* are — a Nancy."

Manx left again, and Brandt tucked the slip of paper he had given him into a pocket.

"Who would know if anybody's doing any research on air emboli?" I asked.

"You mean the air getting into the brain? Clover might. That isn't his specialty, but he has a lot of pipelines. Why?"

"I was just thinking about it."

What I was thinking was that I might do some research on the problem myself. But now my interest in research was not merely a means of attracting Dr. Clover's interest. I was still thinking about Philip Meehan. Or, more like it, all the other Philip Meehans that I might lose.

Seven

IN EARLY NOVEMBER, Oscar Dardin came back to us. He had a broken leg, which, ordinarily, would not have been important. But in Oscar Dardin's case it was, in a sense, everything.

Oscar Dardin was Dr. Gar's patient. But there was more to his illness than surgery, and the other elements were handled by Dr. Tom Johnson, an internist.

Dardin was sixty-two, but you'd have guessed him to be at least eighty. He looked as if he had been left in the oven too long. He was dried and wrinkly, almost an actual case of skin and bones. His hair was gone; his head looked like a skull. His hands were spidery. He was slowly shrinking away.

I had met him when I was a first-year resident. He had had a metastatic cancer of the prostate, and the prostate gland had been removed. Two years later, he came back to us complaining of pain in his bones. The X-rays showed areas of increased bone density and the serum acid phosphatase (a test of metastatic prostatic cancer) was elevated. He was admitted to the hospital and castrated — the treatment for this disease.

After that, he had a good remission. He felt good and even took a trip to Florida (Dr. Gar got a series of postcards). But a few months later he came back. He was having pain again, and when we took X-rays we found that the disease was progressing. This time, he was started on estrogen (female hormone). His voice became higher-pitched and his breast tissues began to enlarge. But he couldn't rightfully complain, since the growth rate of the disease was slowed.

Now, however, he was back.

Dr. Gar set his broken leg, and I assisted, but the broken leg wasn't the problem, it was merely a consequence. Dardin's bones were being eaten away by the tumor.

Dr. Gar and I went to see him after he had been sent down from Recovery. He was in a two-bed room. The other bed at the moment was empty.

"Oscar," Dr. Gar said, "you're going to have to stay with us a while."

"How long?" Dardin asked. His voice was little more than a squeak. "Couldn't you put some plaster of Paris on that leg?"

"When I say a while, I mean a long while," Dr. Gar said. "You don't want to leave here, anyway, do you? We can keep that pain under some control as long as we have you here."

Dardin nodded. "Yes, it's better here," he said.

Dr. Gar had put him on narcotics to ease the pain.

"I just want you to start getting used to the idea — of staying for a good long while," Dr. Gar said. "If you make up your mind to it, it won't be so tough."

Dardin looked distressed. "I'd rather fix my mind on when I can get out," he said. "Could you give me some idea? I find that if a man don't have something to head for, he don't do any heading. He just sort of slogs. Know what I mean? There's got to be something up ahead to aim at. But that 'good long while,' that's kind of hard to pin down."

"Let's say this," Dr. Gar replied. "Let's say that in a couple of months we'll try to make a closer estimate. That's about the best I can do for you right now."

"Well, if you can't get the cake, take a crumb," Dardin said.

We left him then and went to the small waiting room down the corridor where his son and daughter were waiting. His wife had died about ten years earlier.

This was the first time I had met his children. They were in their thirties. The son was good-looking and well-dressed. He was tall and lean, with well-defined features, and a quick look of intelligence in his eyes. The girl was rather plump, but, she, too, was well-dressed. Of the two, she seemed to be the most visibly concerned.

We sat down, and Dr. Gar told them that the setting of the leg had gone well. "But, of course, you realize that that isn't what we're up against," he said.

They both nodded.

"I haven't told your father," Dr. Gar went on. "But it's a matter of months now. The disease has progressed too far. There's nothing we can do about it — except to keep him on narcotics and reduce the pain as much as possible."

"But that isn't final, is it?" the son said.

Dr. Gar thought the son hadn't understood what he had told him. So he repeated it.

The son nodded again, then said, "But what I mean is, there's always a chance, isn't there, that something might change? Isn't it possible that he might take a turn for the better?"

"No, not in this case," Dr. Gar said. "The tumor has gone too far. There's no stopping it."

"But new developments come up every day," the daughter said.

"I wouldn't put too much faith in that," Dr. Gar said. "Even if a cure for this particular kind of cancer were devised tomorrow, it would be too late for your father. Is that what you meant?"

"Well . . . yes, or something else," the daughter said.

"That's right. Who knows what might happen?" the son said. "Things happen all the time."

"What, for instance, in this case?" Dr. Gar asked.

The son shrugged. "I don't know. You're the doctor. All I'm suggesting is, something might happen."

Dr. Gar was silent for a second, then he said, "I'm told that miracles *have* happened. But I don't think it's likely — in this case."

The son and daughter looked at each other. Then the son faced back to Dr. Gar. "All right," he said. "We'll accept that. But miracles do happen. Now, about Father, how much have you told him?"

"So far, only that he'll have to stay here a long while," Dr. Gar replied.

"Good, good. Then I don't think he ought to be told your theory."

"You mean that —"

"Yes, that this is final," the son broke in. "Father has never accepted final decisions. And with good results. If he had taken other people's opinions as final, he would never have done a lot of the things he's done. He brought us up that way, too. Personally, I know you think you're right, Doctor, but I'd like to believe that there's a possibility that you're wrong. We'd like to work on that basis, and it would be better if Father believed that, too."

Dr. Gar smiled slightly. "You say 'work' on that basis. Do what?"

"I'm not sure right now," the son said. "This is just the beginning, we haven't started yet."

"Your father is my patient," Dr. Gar said. "Anything you have in mind, I want to know about it."

"Of course," the daughter said. "We wouldn't do anything — we *couldn't* do anything — without your cooperation."

"Well . . . I'll be interested," Dr. Gar said.

"Are we agreed on this one thing?" the son said. "Father will not be told your opinion."

Dr. Gar nodded. "All right. I have no objection to that."

The son and daughter seemed greatly relieved, even optimistic now.

We walked with them to their father's room, then left them, and headed back toward Surgery.

"Isn't that breaking your rule?" I said to Dr. Gar.

"What rule is that?"

"About telling the patient the truth about his condition."

"I didn't know that was a rule of mine," he said.

"I remember Mr. Foster," I said. "You wanted Dr. Parmalee to tell him the truth."

"*That* was Mr. Foster," he said. "*This* is Mr. Dardin. I don't have a rule about truth. Or, if I do, it is that the best rule is not to have a rule. I believed that Mr. Foster should be told because I thought he could accept it and that he would *want* to know. This is a different case, a different man. Mr. Foster was a realist — he was comfortable with facts. Mr. Dardin, I suspect, is not. I think he would like to believe that there is no challenge that is insurmountable — no mountain that can't be climbed. Well, if that's what he wants to believe, why shouldn't he? Because I have a rule?" He shook his head. "Let him believe. Let *them* believe."

The rest of the way, I thought about that, and decided that he was right.

When we reached Surgery, we parted. I had patients

to see, but instead of visiting them, I went to the library. I had begun a search for information on the act-of-chance that had destroyed Philip Meehan, and in the last few weeks, I had collected a considerable amount of data. In the back of my mind, I had a notion of finding a sure way to prevent air emboli.

My project was not too highly thought of at home. I was spending too many nights in the library.

"What color are Peter's eyes?" Sue said to me one night when I came in very late.

It was dark in the bedroom. I had thought she was asleep. Her voice, unexpected in the darkness, caught me off guard.

"Blue?" I guessed. Actually, it was an unfair question. If I had been sitting staring at our son from the time of his birth, I wouldn't have known what color his eyes were. Eye color was not a thing I noticed.

"Gray," she replied.

"All right — I was close."

"How long since you've seen him?" she said.

"Two days ago — on Sunday."

"You were curled up in the chair all day Sunday with that collection of papers. You didn't *see* him. He was there, but you didn't *see* him."

I was undressed by then, and I got into bed. "Do you know what time I have to get up?" I said. "Can't we save it?"

"For when? I don't see you long enough to fight with you any more."

"Thank God for small favors."

"It isn't going to do you any good, you know," she said. "You could research your head off, and it wouldn't do any good. Clover isn't going to fall for it. You're not a researcher."

"That isn't my reason," I said. "And what's a researcher? Who says I'm not? How do you tell a researcher from anyone else?"

"Patience for one thing."

"Then I'm a researcher. I'm listening to you instead of getting my sleep. That is patience."

"George Bruner plays football with his children," she said.

"Jesus Christ!"

She didn't say anything more about the matter that night. But she might as well have kept it up. I didn't get much sleep anyway.

I had been in the library no more than ten minutes when I heard my name on the squawk box. Nowhere was there any peace from that infernal machine. I put away the journals I had taken out to study and went to the phone. I was wanted for a consult.

When I got to the medical floor, the resident who had called me told me he had an eighty-nine-year-old male on the examining table. The man had come in complaining of vomiting and severe abdominal pain.

We went into the examining room. The man was stretched out, looking like yesterday's cadaver. I checked out the abdominal area and found, as the medical resident had, that it was extremely tender. The patient still had his appendix, and I suspected that it was diseased.

The resident and I talked it over and decided on X-rays. We wheeled the man down to the X-ray room and took a few shots. When we looked at the plates we saw what looked like a partial obstruction of the bowel. It wasn't complete, because we could see air through the picture.

So we went back and talked to the man.

"How long since you've had a bowel movement?" I asked.

He looked puzzled for a second, then said, "Well, off and on."

I held up his history. "You told the intern just yesterday," I said.

He nodded. "Yes. Yesterday."

"Was it hard?"

"Well . . . yes and no."

"Soft, then?"

"Maybe. You might say that."

An idea suddenly hit me. "Where were you when it happened?" I asked.

He looked blank. Then he said, somewhat hesitantly, "In the kitchen?" He wasn't telling me, he was asking me.

I realized that my sudden inspiration was right. He didn't know what I was talking about. He didn't know what the term bowel movement meant.

"All right, one more thing," I said. "When did you last have a crap?"

He frowned. "Long time. Days. Long time."

I handed the history back to the resident.

We wheeled the patient into a ward and put him to bed.

Then we called an intern who was faced with the unpleasant task of loosening the impaction digitally.

I felt sorry for the old man. He looked acutely uncomfortable — but my real sympathies lay with the intern.

I scrubbed twice that afternoon, with no time between scrubs. When I finished the second operation, I stopped in at the lounge for five minutes of just sitting — no thinking — before I went back to the library.

But I had relaxed for about five seconds when

George Bruner came in, interrupting. He looked depressed.

"We just opened a guy, twenty-six, all shot through with the crummy stuff," he said, flopping down on the couch.

I closed my eyes, trying to pretend I wanted to nap.

"Twenty-six, that could've been me," George said. "My God, twenty-six. All chewed up like he'd had a bucket of acid sloshing around in him. I don't know how the hell he got to the hospital. I don't know how the hell he got to be twenty-six. He sure as hell won't get to be twenty-seven."

I kept quiet.

"Marge says Sue says you're doing some research," he said.

"Yeah."

"Have you let Clover in on it?"

I opened my eyes and glared at him. "I'm not doing it for Clover," I said.

"Yeah, well, it was just a thought. But I doubt if it'll ever do you any good. I think Clover probably ties you up with Gar. So, I wouldn't waste a lot of time on it if I were you."

"It has nothing to do with Clover," I insisted.

Bruner ignored the protest. "Because Clover is putting the squeeze on Gar," he said. "And if he connects you with Gar, I don't think any research you do will make any difference."

I sat up. "Putting the squeeze on how?"

"Well, the way I hear it, Gar had some ideas about a new layout for the operating rooms. Did you hear about that? There's talk about some shifting around. Anyway, Gar put his ideas down on paper, sent it to Clover, and there it sits."

"There it sits where?"

"On that desk Clover has in Administration. I guess he hasn't even picked it up and looked at it."

I settled back. "Now that means a hell of a lot, doesn't it?"

"Manx says that's the way they ease people out."

"Where did you get this?" I asked. "Who started it?"

He shrugged. "Who knows? I heard it from — Damned if I know. But Manx says that's the way they do it."

"When are they going to begin this shifting?" I said.

"How do I know? Sometime."

"Sometime. You mean next year? Or the next? Or five years from now?"

"All I know is 'sometime.'"

"So why should Clover be in a hurry to read a lot of ideas on it? He probably will when he gets around to it. Did it ever occur to you that he has a couple of other things to do?"

"I'm just telling you what everybody's saying. Clover is putting on the squeeze."

"Bullshit."

He faced toward me. "What are you sore about?"

"You're talking a lot of crap and you haven't got any evidence," I said.

"The hell. Go see for yourself. Gar's paper's just sitting down there on Clover's desk. Go see for yourself."

"You call that *evidence*?"

"Go see for yourself."

I got up and walked out. I knew that when I got home that night Sue would tell me that Marge had called, and that Marge wanted to know why I was sore at George. It was enough to make me *want* to stay in the library that night.

But, as it happened, I didn't get to the library at all.

After leaving the lounge, I felt the pinch of conscience and headed toward the medical floor to see a couple of patients.

As I stepped out of the elevator, I saw a man who looked to be about thirty-five walking toward me, and pausing every step or two as if trying to catch his breath. But he obviously wasn't a patient. He was dressed in street clothes.

As I reached him, he straightened. Whatever had been bothering him appeared to have passed. He moved on, we passed, and I continued on my way. But when I reached the nurses' station, I stopped and looked back. He had paused again.

"Who's that?" I said to the nurse.

She looked. "Oh . . . That's Mr. Elliot," she said. "His mother was in here. She died about an hour ago. A stroke."

At the same instant that she said "stroke," I saw the man's knees buckle. There was no one near him, and he went down with a thud.

"Get the emergency tray!" I yelled at the nurse.

Then I ran toward the man. At the same time, the elevator door opened and an intern stepped out.

I reached the man about a half-second before the intern did. I rolled him over on his back, stretched his arms upward, and straddled him.

"Breathe for him," I snapped at the intern.

Then I put my hands on the man's chest, one hand on top of the other, and began pressing at an even, steady rate — what I hoped was sixty times per minute, the rate of the normal heart beat.

The intern was now down on his knees, breathing into the man's mouth, filling his lungs at a slower rate, twenty times per minute.

Figures began to appear. I couldn't look up to identify anyone. I had to concentrate on maintaining the steady rate of pressure.

Then someone started counting for me, intoning the word "beat" every second.

That helped. My arms and shoulders were beginning to ache. The counting relieved me of having to maintain the rate in my mind. I could, in effect, turn myself into a non-thinking machine, pressing automatically every time I heard the word "beat."

Time dragged on, but there was no reaction from the man on the floor.

After a while, the intern gave up his place to someone else.

My legs began to cramp.

"You've been at it a half-hour since I've been here," someone said.

The implication was that the man was gone for good.

But it didn't occur to me to stop. I didn't think to myself: the next beat may be the beat that does it. I wasn't thinking at all. My mind had gone numb.

After a while, the aches and cramps went away. I felt light, floating. Someone suggested taking over for me. But I couldn't move. It was physically impossible for me to change from the position I had been in so long.

Perspiration rolled into my eyes. The word "beat" pounded in my brain.

Then I heard someone say "pulse."

A few minutes later, they lifted me off the man. I couldn't stand on my own legs. So someone brought a chair, and they sat me in it.

Sitting there, I saw two orderlies put the man on a stretcher and carry him away.

He was alive. His heart was beating.

Someone asked me if I needed anything. I said no.

I tried again to stand, and this time my legs held. A lot of voices said a lot of things. But all the words got pretty much mixed together, becoming a garble. I told them all that, yes, yes, yes, I was all right. Then one of the interns walked with me to the elevator and rode down with me. I asked him to check me out. He said he would, but he didn't leave. He walked me all the way across the street to the elevator of the apartment building before he finally took his hand from my arm.

When I got upstairs, Sue was in the kitchen.

"You're home?" she called out.

I said, yes, I was home.

"Marge called," she said, coming out of the kitchen. "Why are you sore at George?"

I didn't wait for her to reach me. I went into the bedroom, fell on the bed, and don't remember anything more until the next morning.

Eight

WINTER WAS UNUSUALLY frigid that year. I took it as an omen, although winters in the Midwest are always blustery and cold. But it was a bad time, and I preferred to blame the season rather than myself for my bad mood.

I was devoting every extra second I could snatch to research. Sue, shut in by the weather, became cross and irritable, resenting the fact that she and Peter were receiving very little of my attention.

Guilt was snapping at my heels. Most of the hours I spent on research were taken from the time I wanted to use following up post-operative patients. Not that, strictly speaking, I was failing my duty, but I was cutting down on the extra care that I had always considered an essential part of medicine.

Dr. Gar, too, was aware that I was spending my extra time with books and papers rather than with patients. And, although he did not actually say so, he let me know that he did not approve.

One morning as we left the operating room, he said to me, "I see Mr. Wolsak was back again. An intern saw him."

Mr. Wolsak was an old man of sixty-five who had come into the hospital a few months earlier complaining of a tumor on his leg. Actually, it was only a sebaceous cyst — a plugged hair follicle that had become filled with an oily material. Ordinarily we don't like to cut these cysts. But Wolsak whined so much, and was so fearful of cancer, that we finally operated.

He was my patient. I infiltrated the area with procaine, a local anesthetic, then opened the cyst and shelled it out. I put a drain on it, and gave him an appointment to come back a week later.

He came back, all right. And he had been coming back, week after week, ever since. The drain and the sutures had been removed and the wound had healed well, but Wolsak wasn't satisfied. He insisted that he still had pain, and he was convinced that he had developed cancer because of the operation.

I finally began turning him over to whichever intern was on duty. He was a time-robber, and I said as much to Dr. Gar.

"You're one hundred percent sure, are you, that he's a crank?" he said.

"I couldn't be surer," I said.

"Have you ever been that positive and been wrong?"

"No."

"Then you have something to look forward to," he said. "It's happened to me."

The comment unsettled me a bit. After that, I began seeing Wolsak myself when he came in. My opinion of his complaint didn't change, but my conscience was bothering me.

Looking back, I'm sure Dr. Gar realized that my diagnosis was right. He just wanted to shake me up. He didn't like overconfidence. He was afraid it led to errors.

That was why, I supposed, he always followed up closely on his own patients. He wanted to reduce the possibility of error to the absolute minimum. It was his way of being a good surgeon, a good doctor. And evidently he wanted me to be the same.

Just before Christmas we got a note asking us to Dr. Mackey's annual party. The invitation was expected. It always went to the senior residents. It was official recognition that we were deemed fit to socialize — at least for one night — with attendings.

The party was held at Dr. Mackey's home, which was a junior-sized mansion located north of the city on the lake. Sue and I rode out with the Bruners. Our car had recently collapsed and we couldn't afford any major repairs.

"This is the third step," George said as we swung out along the drive that followed the lake. "First you get your bachelor degree, then you get your M.D., then you get your invitation to Mackey's Christmas party. After this, we're set — we can practice anywhere."

"It's a farce," Sue said. "Dr. Mackey wouldn't even know any of you if he saw you — would he?"

98

"That's not the point," Marge said. "It's a ceremony — like baptism."

"Right. Only it's done with booze instead of water," George said.

"It's a farce," Sue repeated.

"No more than going to church once a year at Christmas," Marge said. "It holds the whole thing together, like church once a year and Christianity. Only this is the medical profession."

Sue hunched down in the corner of the seat and became silent. She was not in one of her better moods.

"One thing," George said to me, "you'll see what I mean about Gar and Clover tonight. If they're both there."

"I wouldn't expect anything," I said. "In the first place, you don't know that they're feuding. And in the second place, they wouldn't do it at Mackey's."

"Booze," George said.

"What does booze have to do with it?"

"Inhibitions."

"Make some sense, will you?"

"When you get a couple of shots of booze in you, you loosen up. The 'real you' comes out. I don't care what you say about Gar and Clover, they're human. A couple shots of booze and they're as human as anybody."

"And you know what they say about Mackey's," Marge said to George.

"Right," George said. "At Mackey's the booze flows like wine. What he does is figure out how much liquor he'll need for the whole year, then he buys it all and charges it up to this party so he can take it off his income tax — like an expense."

"And that's what holds the medical profession together — like Christianity," Sue gloomed.

We got lost looking for Dr. Mackey's home and wasted almost an hour following George's infallible instinct, so the party was in full swing by the time we arrived.

We were met at the door by a butler (whether permanent or hired for the night, I'm not sure), then taken over to Mrs. Mackey. She was a small, fluttery woman, with a distant look in her eyes. She listened carefully as we told her our names and said that since we knew everyone present — which wasn't strictly true — there was no point in introducing us to the others. Then she fluttered off.

A number of young men in white coats were weaving in and out among the guests with trays of drinks. We stopped one of them, armed ourselves, and surveyed the scene.

"There's Gar," George said, pointing one way. "And there's Clover," he said, pointing in the opposite direction. "They must still be on their first drink."

"Does Dr. Mackey have a pool?" Marge said. "I'd like to see somebody pushed in the pool."

I caught a glimpse of Dr. Mackey. He was running, as usual.

Then I saw Paul Brandt. He was with a stunning blonde and they were in earnest conversation.

Lou Manx came up to us. "There's dancing in the West Wing," he said to me. "Let me borrow your wife for a twist."

"Where's your own twist?" I asked.

"I'm stag," he said. "Brandt and I flipped for Peggy tonight, and I lost."

"Is that her name — Peggy?" I said, nodding toward the blonde. She didn't look like a Peggy. She was too sleek.

"Tonight, she's Peggy," Manx replied. "In fact, she's

been Peggy since a week ago Monday. Before that she was Nicole. She's searching for her true identity. She can't decide whether she's Theda Bara or Minnie Mouse. Tonight, it's Minnie Mouse."

"Doesn't she mind being shared?" Marge said.

"Why? When the choice is between a movie producer's son and a Broadway producer's son? She's an actress. Actresses have to suffer."

"Who's the —" Marge began.

But Manx was taking Sue away.

George began explaining to his wife that — for the purposes of the drama — Paul Brandt's father was in Hollywood and Lou's in New York. Since I knew the details, I drifted away.

I wandered through the room, acknowledging greetings here and there. Spirits were high. There was a great deal of abnormally loud laughter. I saw that all of the heads of departments were present. Most of the conversations I overheard were limited to shop talk. It was a lot like a medical seminar with liquor.

I finally came to the West Wing. There was a four-piece combo. The room was large and had a tile floor. The couples were all twisting. I saw Sue and Lou Manx, but they were involved in the intricacies of the dance and didn't see me. So I drifted again.

As I was looking for the bar, I bumped into Tris Maney. He was limping.

"What did you do, put your foot in it?" I said.

He grimaced. "Tendon," he said. "The only reason I came tonight was so I could twist. And look at me. Tendon."

"Have a drink," I suggested. "It's the best thing in the world for a tendon."

Maney didn't drink. I knew that. And he knew I knew it. But he explained to me, anyway, that he didn't. And told me why — which I also knew. He had a theory that alcohol fed on white corpuscles.

I excused myself, and left him to enjoy his misery. I got a fresh drink and joined a couple of medical residents who were talking about liver failures — a natural subject with all that liquor around. After a few minutes, I managed to switch the conversation to Philip Meehan's embolism. I picked their brains for everything they knew on the subject.

A little later, Sue returned — without Lou Manx, but with a new enthusiasm. She had developed a fascination for the twist, and, having worn out Lou Manx, she wanted me to join her on the dance floor. I fought — and lost. And, for the next hour or so, I subjected myself to a physical excess that struck me as madness.

When we finally left the dance floor and went after some liquid refreshment we met Lou Manx and Peggy (she was still Peggy). Paul Brandt was nowhere in sight.

"Your wife is related to the Marquis de Sade," Manx said.

Sue was flushed and breathing hard — but happy. "That *is* fun!" she said.

"I'm crazy about it, too," Peggy said. "But I don't do it in public. I'm exhibitionistic."

We all looked at her for an explanation.

"I bounce in front," she said, indicating her bosom. "If you're endowed, sometimes it takes half the fun out of getting there. Know what I mean?"

We shook our heads.

"People gape," she explained.

"Gape how?" Manx asked.

"They gape at you. If you're endowed and you bounce, people stop and gape."

"Gape?" he said.

She nodded. "Is that what it is?"

"Where is Paul?" I asked.

"He had a call from nature," Peggy said. "Lou is overlooking me while he's gone."

"Overseeing," Lou explained to me. "That's the rule — when Paul gets a call from nature, I oversee the property and vice versa. We don't dare let it out of our sight."

Peggy giggled. "I feel like a girl in a gilded cage," she said, "always being watched. But it's a very nice sort of kind of protection, and kind of cute. Maybe you didn't know, but I used to go steady — as the saying goes — with Lou. Then I fell madly in love with Paul, so now it's even-Steven."

"Steve is the other guy," Lou said.

Peggy giggled again. "Lou always says that. But there isn't anybody else. Just Paul. When I heard the story about Paul and his father — how they don't communicate — it was love at first sight."

"That's Paul's father the movie producer," Lou explained to Sue and me.

"Isn't it almost *like* a movie?" Peggy said. "Paul wanting to be a doctor, and his father wanting him to be a producer in his footsteps? It's just like that fellow with the curly hair and the violin."

We turned to Lou for a translation.

He shrugged. "Don't ask me."

At that point, Paul joined us.

"Where did you leave your violin?" Lou asked him.

"With my curly hair," he replied. Peggy's dialogue was apparently limited.

"Do you twist?" Sue said to him.

"I do, but I can't now," Brandt replied. He seemed

genuinely sorry. He indicated Peggy. "I'm on duty," he explained.

"Don't you like the way he kids," Peggy giggled. "You'd never believe he was a serious doctor."

"Sometimes I don't think I'm cut out for the role," Brandt said. "A joke or a quip always at the ready — it's not the doctor image. I may decide yet to produce movies."

George Bruner came up. "They closing in," he said.

"Do you twist?" Sue asked him.

He nodded. "I say I twist. Marge says I just do a bad foxtrot."

"Who's closing in?" I asked.

He gestured behind him. "Remember when we came in, Gar was over there and Clover was over there. Now, they're together."

I looked. Gar and Clover were seated in chairs, facing each other, circled by a number of residents and attendings.

"Then let's go," I heard Sue say.

When I turned back, I saw her dragging George toward the room where the combo was playing.

"Well, I don't see why I should suffer just because some people don't have manners," Peggy said. "I can't help it if they want to gape."

"That's 'gap,'" Paul said.

"No, honey, it's 'gape.' Lou said." She took his hand. "Let's twist."

"That's right," Lou said. "Damn the torpedoes, let the eyeballs fall where they may."

Paul and Peggy followed Sue and George toward the dance floor.

Lou nodded in the direction of Gar and Clover. "Shall we mosey over?" he smiled.

It was too tempting to resist. We moseyed.

We stopped just outside the circle that surrounded Gar and Clover. If we expected fireworks, we were disappointed. They were talking amiably, discussing the broad subject of heart failure. Clover argued that women suffer fewer heart diseases because the female hormone, estrogen, acts as a safeguard. Gar claimed that the attempts to guard men against heart failure by injecting estrogen had, so far, proved inconclusive.

It was fairly unexciting shop talk. I began to get edgy and started to think about finding Sue and talking her into finding Marge and talking her into finding George and talking him into leaving. That's the roundabout way you have to go about things when your own car is dead and you're riding as a passenger.

But then Clover mentioned the fellowship.

Lou dug me in the ribs. "Here we go," he said. His antenna was quivering.

"It's a fine thing," Dr. Clover said. "An extra year to learn. I wish I'd had it when I was a resident. An extra year of research can mean a lot. Sometimes when you're on a project, that's all you need, a little more time."

"Of course, the fellowship was meant for a man who intends to practice," Dr. Gar said.

"Yes. But that can be translated liberally," Clover replied. "What, actually, is meant by the term 'practice'?"

Dr. Gar looked at him evenly. "I didn't know there was any question about the meaning of the term."

"Well, practice means doing, doesn't it? And a man who is working on a project is certainly doing something."

"I doubt if that's what the founders intended," Dr. Gar said.

"I think it's open to interpretation."

"Then, of course, you have to ask yourself — am I interpreting or corrupting?"

"Yes, yes," Clover agreed. "But all rules must be subject to some degree of interpretation. I've never liked to hog-tie myself with absolutes. You're the same way, Max."

They kept that up for a while, not really saying anything. The significant point was that Clover did not feel that the fellowship had to be awarded to a resident who intended to practice.

"He's giving himself an out," Manx said, as we moved away. "He's already decided to give the fellowship to a researcher. He's making his excuse now, so the announcement won't be such a blow when it actually comes."

"Maybe not," I said. "Maybe that's the way he feels. And maybe he's right."

"Cut it out," Lou said. "Your wound is showing."

"No, looking at it objectively, I think he *is* right," I said. "If he thinks a researcher should have the fellowship — why not? I think Gar agrees with him."

I lifted a fresh drink off a passing tray.

"I don't blame you," Lou said, "I'd get drunk, too."

"I have no intention of getting drunk."

"Then I'll do it for you," Lou smiled. He pushed off through the crowd.

I leaned against a convenient wall and thought about Clover's pronouncement. It seemed as if my chances for getting the fellowship were pretty low, but I had meant it when I had said to Manx that Clover would not be corrupting the intention of the fellowship by giving it to a researcher.

And that brought another thought to mind. I was working on a project myself. Or, at least, I was making passes at it. Why not let Clover know what I was doing? I had an excellent reason for talking to him. In fact, Paul Brandt had suggested it. He had said that Clover, with all his pipelines, might know of other work being done in the same area. But the more I thought of approaching Clover, the less I liked the idea. He'd probably know exactly what I was up to.

About then, Sue came along. "Marge has been trying to talk me into talking you into talking George into leaving," she said.

So I went to find George.

He was ready to leave. "Your wife damn near killed me. Get her off that twist kick, will you?"

Later, I decided that no, I wouldn't. She had apparently twisted all the hostility out of her system on the dance floor. And, driving home, in the back seat, we made out like lovers. It was nice to have her back.

Nine

THE NEW YEAR began with Mrs. Cuckoo. That, she insisted, was her name, and we had to take her word for it.

Within hours the whole hospital knew that Medicine had acquired a fruitcake. She was admitted with a huge mass in her right breast and a severely ulcerated nipple. She also had a tumorous lymph node in her neck. The condition had begun three years earlier with a small lump but she had refused to see a doctor until two days ago.

She was still totally unconcerned. Her condition did not bother her in the least. Nor did anything else, including the hospital rules.

The first story that made the rounds was that she had left her room, found the stairway to the roof, and spent the afternoon pelting visitors with snowballs.

Next, I heard that she was sending telegrams to the heads of various foreign governments, charging the calls to the hospital phone. The messages were really crazy. The telegram to the Prime Minister of Great Britain, for example, read: HOW I WOULD HAVE LOVED TO HAVE KNOWN RUDYARD KIPLING.

When I was called in to consult on the case, I expected to find a wild-eyed maniac. But nothing could have been farther from the facts. Mrs. Cuckoo was short and somewhat plump, with a round, sweet, smiling face. Her age on her history read fifty-five, and that seemed about right. She was graying, but only slightly.

As I came in the door, she said, "Do you remember fresh bread?"

As a matter of fact, I did remember fresh bread. My mother had once gone on a baking kick, and the smell of freshly baked bread had delighted me. I could still recall it, I told Mrs. Cuckoo.

"Oh, that," she said. "Yes, everyone remembers that. What I meant was, fresh bread was so coarse. Now, myself, I like the store bread. It doesn't have the odor, granted. But, frankly, I think that odor was overrated. Too much of it was sickening. Open the windows, for heaven's sake. Actually, what I had in mind was texture. Store bread is so smooth and soft. Especially if you get it in the morning. You can poke a finger right through it. What a joy! I wonder if the kitchen would send me up a slice? I haven't poked my finger through a slice of bread in . . . oh, in a long time."

I let the matter drop and began my examination.

"Try not to think about it," she said.

"About what?"

"My condition. If you think about it, you'll just get yourself upset. The other doctors—Dr. Morrissey, poor boy—they take disease so seriously. That's the trouble today, we take so many things so seriously. Saving face, for instance. Are you aware, Doctor, that in 1732 one Abner Harrison murdered a small child in order to save face? The child was born to his wife, but he wasn't the father of it."

"No, I wasn't aware of that," I replied.

"See? What a silly thing to do. He saved face, but, now, all these years later, who knows about it? People don't even remember Abner Harrison, let alone his silly face."

I excused myself, went to the nurses' station, and called for a stretcher and an orderly to take Mrs. Cuckoo to an examining room. Then I went back to the ward.

"You *are* worried," she said to me. "What a shame." She closed her eyes for a second, then opened them again, smiling once more. "You don't read enough Kipling," she said.

I sat down in the chair by the bed. "Kipling isn't in favor right now," I smiled. "He was an imperialist."

"Oh, it doesn't matter what he said. It's the way he said it. His style. A marvelous beat. Like a marching band. Trumpets blaring. Drums booming. What an ass! That's the wonderful thing about him. So obviously, so patently an ass! We don't have poets like that today. They're all such very nice people. Not an ass among them."

"I don't think I quite understand that," I said.

"Why, it's such a joy. To read Kipling. And to be stirred up by all the emotion. Those trumpets, those drums. Then, a moment later, after the trumpets and drums have gone, to be able to sigh very deeply and say, 'What an ass!' *That* is the true value of poetry. To be able, in the end, to say with clear conviction that the poet himself is a consummate ass. Oh, how lovely for the soul!"

The orderly and the stretcher arrived and we lifted Mrs. Cuckoo aboard it. In the examining room, I did a needle biopsy, then sent her back to the ward. When the report came back, it confirmed our suspicion that the disease had already gone too far. It was too late to remove the breast. I wrote an order to keep her in the hospital for observation, and to begin radiation treatment. She had, I guessed, at the outside, six more months to live.

Two days later, I was told that Mrs. Cuckoo had somehow got hold of her clothes and that she had left the hospital. On checking the address she had given, Administration found it to be an office building, and no one in the building had ever heard of her. I assumed that I had seen the last of her.

Oscar Dardin, the man with prostatic cancer, who refused to accept the seriousness of his condition, was growing weaker. He was on drugs now, and his body was more or less in a state of suspension. But his mind was clear. He was still expecting to leave the hospital soon.

I received a call from his daughter one day, and she made an appointment to see me that same afternoon. I met her—and her brother, who had come along—in the main lobby. We sat in a corner and talked in lowered tones.

"We brought you this," the daughter said, handing me a page from a newsmagazine. "Maybe you know about it, but we want to be sure."

I read the story, which I had not seen. It concerned an experimental cancer treatment. The treatment was not new to me, however. I had read a paper on it.

"Yes?" I said, handing back the page.

"Can you use it?" the son asked. "To help Father?"

I shook my head. "I'm sorry, no. This applies to a carcinoma in its very early stages." I pointed to the page. "It says that in there."

"Yes, but we thought the theory might be applied in some way," the daughter said.

I shook my head again.

They exchanged looks. Then the son said, "There's another matter. Father has a private room, and the expense is getting a little out of hand. We wondered if some arrangement could be made."

"For instance?"

"We don't know."

"You could talk to a social worker," I said. "You might be able to transfer him to a ward. The care is the same, only it's free."

Again, they looked at each other.

Then the son said, "Would he be moved out of his room?"

"Yes, into a ward."

"Couldn't we get the same thing, only not move him out of his room?" the daughter asked.

"That wouldn't be the *same* thing," I pointed out.

"I'm thinking of the psychological effect," the son said. "His morale—if he were moved—we have to think about that."

111

"The wards aren't that much different," I said. The patients get the same treatment, the same food, the same everything."

"It's the moving she means," the son explained. "Taking him from one place and putting him in another. It's like . . . well, losing faith. You see, it depends on . . . " He looked distressed, pulling on his chin, as if he had lost the words.

"On believing, and sticking to it," the daughter said. "On not backing down. But moving him from his room to a ward, that would be like taking a step backwards. It would be like admitting that he's losing ground."

"Have you seen him lately?" I said. "He is losing ground."

She shook her head. "That's temporary."

"Well, the only thing I can suggest," I said, "is that you talk to Administration. Maybe something can be worked out."

That seemed to encourage them. I took them to the bursar's office and left them there. But I doubted that their plea would get any more than a hearing. Administration dealt in facts.

When I left them, I went to their father's room. He seemed to be disappearing, rapidly shrinking away. His shriveled body in the bed hardly disturbed the sheets.

"We're reaching the crisis," he said to me. His voice, as a result of the injections of estrogen and his weakness, was a high, thin whisper. "This is what I've been waiting for—the crisis. You have to have the crisis, 'fore you can turn the corner."

I nodded, smiling, trying not to show what I felt.

"I give it another couple days," he said. "We're working up to the peak now. It always gets worse before it gets better. You have to fight. That's all that's

112

left. You and Death. Hand to hand and tooth to tooth. That's the crisis."

"Yes, sir," I said.

"Oh, the sunlight," he sighed.

"What, sir?"

"That's the reward. When you fight and win, then suddenly, there's the sunlight. The crisis is passed, and there's the sunlight."

I nodded again.

"A couple more days," he said. "Then we'll pass the crisis."

"Yes, sir."

I left him.

I had some time, so I went to the library, but my mind kept going back to Oscar Dardin. I remembered what Dr. Gar had said about miracles, but I couldn't make myself believe that Dardin had a chance.

I dragged my mind back to the paper in front of me and found that I had already read it. This had happened before. For several days now, I had been *re*-reading rather than reading. The fact was that I had exhausted all the Journals on the subject and had begun backtracking.

I forced myself to admit that what I was really doing was delaying. It was time to take the next step. To search for further information outside the library, or to begin experimenting with the knowledge I already had.

But neither course really interested me. Which forced me to make another admission. Research was not my field. I did not have the incentive, I did not have the patience. My only ambition was to stand at the table, to be a practicing surgeon. That was the extent and the limit of my desire.

113

I put the journal back in the file and left the library. Then I went to Administration.

After being passed from clerk to clerk, I finally found the woman who had seen the Dardins. She said that they had asked if their father could be considered a ward patient, but left in his private room. She had referred them to a social worker.

"But it's impossible, of course," she said.

"Would it help if I made a recommendation?" I asked.

She thought for a second, then said, "If you demanded it, Doctor, I suppose we might arrange something. *Is* it necessary?"

"It would make it easier for him," I replied.

"Is it necessary?" she asked again.

"I just think it would be better."

"Why don't you talk to your head of department?" she suggested.

That put the matter right back where it had been before.

For two days, I did nothing, but each time I saw Oscar Dardin I became more determined to keep him in his private room.

On the third day, I went to see Dr. Clover. He was out of town.

"Is it important?" his secretary said. "You could see Dr. Gar."

So I cornered Gar.

I told him what I wanted, and why. He didn't answer immediately. It was near lunchtime, and he suggested that we go to the cafeteria and eat. On the way down, he talked about a case that we were going to operate on the next day.

When we were at the table, eating, he finally answered me.

"No," he said. "I wouldn't authorize it, and I'm sure Dr. Clover wouldn't."

I thought he didn't understand why I wanted Dardin to remain in the room. So I repeated my argument.

He shook his head. "There is no medical reason for not moving him," he said. "Mr. Dardin is going to die. Moving him or not moving him will have absolutely no effect on that."

"I don't think you understand yet. The point is—"

"The point is that you think it would be easier for Mr. Dardin to sustain his belief if he remained in his own room. I understand that. But Mr. Dardin's belief is his belief. It isn't mine. It isn't yours. It isn't Dr. Clover's. It's Mr. Dardin's belief—his and his alone. I don't deny his right to it, but on the other hand, I have no responsibility to alter the rules of the hospital to support and encourage it."

I felt my temper rising. "Would it hurt the goddamn hospital *that* much to have him in that room a few days more?" I said.

"The hospital would survive," Gar replied evenly.

"Then why can't he stay there?"

"Because there is no medical reason for it. I am willing, at any time, to stand up to Administration when there is a medical reason at stake. But this is *not* such an instance."

"That man up there is fighting, I think it's our duty to help him."

"To help him sustain a delusion?"

"Why not? He's dying."

"Because this is not the best of all possible worlds," Gar replied. "Often—quite often—it's an unfair and unfeeling world. There are times when it has to put sympathy aside for the sake of order. Call it cold,

115

call it cruel, but when you reach my age, you'll have more respect for order than you do now."

I didn't argue any more. I frankly wasn't convinced that he was right. But I realized there was nothing I could do. Order—for right or wrong—had prevailed.

Later that week, Oscar Dardin was transferred to a ward. But by then the question of whether or not he should be moved was irrelevant. He was conscious only for scant minutes at a time. He wasn't aware, I am sure, that he was being shifted from one room to another. At least, the move had no noticeable effect. He had been failing fast before, and he continued at the same pace.

Having dropped my research, I became involved with other patients. Consequently, Oscar Dardin became less and less a personal concern. That, too, was part of the order, I suppose. Order commands that a person proceed, move on to the next task. And, in moving on, the yesterdays fall further and further behind.

The release from research, of course, gave me more time at home, too. Sue and I tried to make up for the last months. Every night that I was free, we went somewhere—to a movie, to a play (there was a theater not far from the hospital where a group of young actors, struggling against the inevitable, were trying to make a commercial success of Ibsen), to dinner.

Finally, walking home one night, Sue begged for relief.

"I'm tired," she said. "How long are we going to run?"

"What are you kicking about now? First you complained because I spent every night in the library,

116

now you're complaining because we're doing a little catching up."

"I'm tired," she said again.

"What do you want?"

"I just want to stay home one night."

"All right, we'll stay home."

"We can't even afford this," she said. "If you have to get something out of your system, pick some cheaper way, can't you?"

"Money. It has its fingers in everything."

"Is that supposed to be news?"

I told her about Dardin. About what I had wanted to do. And about Gar's decision.

She was quiet for a while. We just walked. Winter was showing signs of passing; it was one of those autumn nights that sometimes occur in the middle of January; out of place, but appreciated.

Then she said, "It does seem like he was being awfully stubborn."

"It doesn't make any difference now," I told her. "Dardin was moved and he didn't even know it."

"That doesn't change what was right and wrong."

"No."

"Has it changed the way you think about Dr. Gar?"

"I don't know."

"He could be wrong about something and still be the same person," she said.

"Well, it doesn't matter."

"Are you sorry you stopped your research, then? Is that it?"

"I guess I'm a little disappointed in myself," I said. "I had such goddamn good intentions. The problem is there, and somebody ought to do something about it. Somebody will, I guess. But I thought it was going to be me. I saw myself saving all the Philip Meehans."

117

"Like the doctor in the movie? With the music in the background and all that?"

"Maybe. Like that a little, I guess."

"Then you didn't have the right reason," she said. You know I suspect that the people who make the glamorous discoveries are very undramatic people. They just go on finding out answers to problems and don't even think about what the end will be."

"Paul Brandt said something like that."

"It's probably not always the case," she said. "God, I guess somebody at some time has been inspired. But I'll bet that most of them haven't. I'll bet they were just doing what they liked to do. But you weren't. Do you see? Your reason was wrong."

"I suppose."

"Then be yourself," she said.

I felt a little better. At least, I didn't dislike myself quite as much.

Two days later, Oscar Dardin died. It wasn't a dramatic death. He simply stopped living.

I saw the son and daughter when they came to the hospital to take care of the arrangements. Strangely— or so I thought—they seemed relieved. The grimness was gone from their faces. Apparently living with their father's faith had been a considerable burden. I realized then that they hadn't really believed. They had been acting out their parts. As their father had acted out his part. I wondered if they—the father and the children—had ever been honest with each other.

But I was too busy to wonder for very long. The question, like all the others, faded into the distance. And order was restored.

Ten

SPRING. It came that year in a rush. One day the ground was covered with snow, the next day the trees in the nearby park came to bud.

To me, it meant that the time for announcing the winner of the fellowship was drawing closer. Although I had just about counted myself out of the running, spring somehow revived my hope.

There was nothing except the season to base it on. Paul Brandt — by Dr. Clover's special leave—spent less and less time in the operating room, and more and more time in the research building. And Dr. Clover, in his spare time, was now assisting him in his project. The implication was clear that Paul would have Clover's vote.

Then one afternoon in late March I received a call from Dr. Clover to report to his office. His "office" was a desk in Administration that he rarely stopped at. But he was there that day. And when I got to the desk he waved me into a side chair, and handed me a chart.

"Do you know this case?" he said.

I looked at the name on the history, Valerie McCall. "Yes," I replied. "I know the case."

Valerie was a nurse at Briggs. She was twenty-eight, a small, pretty, dark-eyed girl. As a child she had had rheumatic fever. It was a mild case, but it had left her mitral valve (the valve between the two chambers of the heart) impaired. Scar tissue had so narrowed it that blood had trouble passing through. For the past couple of years, according to the history, she had been bothered by mild shortages of breath. Now, she was beginning to cough up small amounts of blood. Because of this, her doctor had recommended having the valve repaired.

"We're going to schedule her for next Thursday," Dr. Clover said. "Since you had six months on cardiac surgery last year, I thought you might like to do the operation."

I was elated. It would be a wonderful opportunity. In such cases, even senior residents generally did no more than assist.

"I'll be at the table with you," Clover said. "But I want you to handle this from beginning to end." He leaned a little forward. "Right now, let's go over the technique. Tell me what you'll do, step by step by step. If I have anything to add or correct, I'll break in."

We sat there for a little over an hour. I "talked" the operation, and, as he had said he would, Dr. Clover added and corrected.

When we finished, he said, "We'll do this again tomorrow." He looked at his watch. "Same time." Then he waved me away, dismissing me.

Later, thinking the matter over, I became curious. Why me? The operation involved a heart valve. Paul Brandt was doing research on heart valves. Why not Paul?

The next morning, between scrubs, sitting in the lounge, I mentioned the matter to Lou Manx. By then, my puzzlement had reached outsized proportions. In fact, I was mildly suspicious.

Manx thought about the question for a moment. Then he said, "It's probably just simple good sense. You can't say Clover doesn't have good sense."

"Good sense how?"

"Put yourself in Clover's shoes. He isn't jealous about his table, he wants to give his residents a chance. He knows that the only way to teach them is to let them do. Okay. He wanted to give the case to one of the residents. But it takes skill. So he wanted the best man."

I suggested that he might have given the chance to Paul Brandt.

"Paul's mind isn't on surgery these days," Lou said.

"It would be if he were standing at the table."

"Then that's it, I suppose. He hasn't spent much time in the operating room lately."

"Maybe," I said. But I wasn't convinced.

That afternoon at the appointed time I went back to Clover's desk. He was there, and we went through the operation again, step by step. This time he simply listened, offering no additions or corrections. Evidently I made no errors.

I arrived at the hospital an hour before I was due that Thursday. I had a quick cup of coffee in the cafeteria, then went to Valerie McCall's room. One of her friends was with her, giving her an injection, the preliminary anesthetic. I made a brief examination, and we joked awhile. Then she began to get a little groggy, so I left.

When I got to the surgical floor, I found that the operation was scheduled for the main operating room which was large, and outfitted with every available mechanical device. And there was a gallery, a balcony where observers could watch the proceedings.

I went to the scrub room. The circulating nurse was there.

"I see we're putting on a show this morning," she

121

said. "I don't think Valerie knows that. I'll bet Dr. Clover didn't tell her."

"What do you mean 'show'?"

"There are about a dozen residents in there," she said.

I went to the door and looked into the operating room. There were about a half-dozen—not a dozen—residents sitting in the gallery.

"What's going on?" I asked. My curiosity was growing by the second.

"I think Dr. Clover handed out invitations," she said. "Boy, if Valerie knew that, she'd do flips."

The intern came in and, being an intern, he began complaining about not getting any sleep. Interns are obsessed with the idea of sleep.

I started scrubbing at another sink. While I was on my fingers, Dr. Clover came in. He was in a good mood. He gave a cheery hello to each and every one of us.

"You'll have an audience this morning," he said to me, stepping up to another sink. "I suggested to some of the residents that it might be interesting to watch. You don't suffer from stage fright, do you?"

"I don't think so," I said.

"I'll bet Valerie would—if she knew," the circulating nurse said. She didn't seem to approve.

Clover chuckled, but offered no further comment. He turned to the intern. "You look like you need some sleep," he said.

It was like turning on a gusher. The intern told us, minute by minute, how little sleep he had had in the past week.

The anesthetist came in, gleefully rubbing his hands together. "What a day!" he enthused. "I'm getting the boat out this weekend."

Clover asked him what kind of boat he had and that started a discussion—sail boats.

When we were finally ready, Clover led the way into the operating room. He glanced up at the gallery, smiling.

Valerie had been brought in and was on the table. She was lying on her right side—left side up—and had been draped. I went to the head of the table and looked at her. She was still slightly conscious, and she forced a thin smile. But I doubt that she really knew what was going on.

Then I stepped into the surgeon's place at the table, and Clover moved to the other side to assist. The anesthetist was scowling at his gauges.

"When you're ready," I said to him.

He inserted the endotracheal tube and began feeding the anesthetic.

A moment or so later, he signaled to me.

I felt perspiration on my forehead. Not because I was unsure of the operation, but because of the eyes staring from the gallery.

"Scalpel."

The instrument was slapped into my hand by the scrub nurse.

I made an incision between the fifth and sixth ribs from the left border of the sternum to the back of the shoulder.

"Clamps."

Clover was a top-notch assistant. He was right there with the clamps.

I cut deeper, through the muscles.

"Clamps."

Clover clamped, then spoke to the anesthetist. "Do you know Frank Brice?" he said. He was referring to Dr. Frank Brice, an attending associated with Briggs.

"Isn't he the thirty-foot Chris-Craft?" the anesthetist asked.

"That's him."

I split the fifth rib, then began applying a spreader to retract the shoulder bone.

"He got hung up on a sandbar last summer," Clover said. "He was there for sixteen hours."

"Where was he—in an inlet?"

"No, alongshore. There were boats flying by, but Brice is the kind who won't ask for help. He wouldn't even wave. He just sat there."

I told the anesthetist to hyperventilate the lungs. When he was through, Clover and I packed down the left lung. This exposed the left heart chamber.

I started a purse-string suture at the base of the chamber to prevent blood from leaking out of the heart after I had opened it.

"He's turning that Chris-Craft into a hotel," Clover said. "Last year he put in a hi-fi system and a dishwasher. He's talking about a garbage disposal now."

The anesthetist laughed.

"Scalpel."

I had finished the suture, and now I made the opening. Clover turned his attention back to the operation.

I held out my right hand to the scrub nurse and she stripped the glove from it. Then she swabbed my index finger with hexaclorothane, a sterilizing solution. I shook my hand in the air to dry it. The bared finger would give me a more sensitive feel. I would have less trouble identifying the opening of the scarred valve than if I used a plain instrument.

Using my left hand to hold the suture, I inserted my finger into the hole I had made in the chamber. The idea was to open the space between the sides of

124

the valves. But it was somewhat tricky. It had to be done without making the passage so wide that it would create a fatal leak.

I eased my finger forward in the space between the valves, and, at the same time, exerted a counter pressure with my thumb, which was on the outside of the heart, against the valve. It was a little like trying to get a penny out of a piggy bank with only one finger inside the bank.

There was dead silence in the operating room. Clover was bending forward, observing, but not apprehensively, only with interest.

I worked my finger farther into the chamber.

"I know a fellow who has an ice cube maker on his boat," the anesthetist said.

Clover ignored him.

"It makes oblong cubes."

My finger found what it was probing for. With a rolling motion, the finger against the thumb, I split the valve.

Clover leaned back, sensing somehow that the job had been done.

"That's a contradiction in terms—oblong cubes," he said to the anesthetist.

While I closed the chamber wall with purse-string sutures, they argued back and forth. The anesthetist claimed that ice cube was a generic term for any small piece of ice, and thus it did not necessarily have to be a true cube. But Clover insisted that if a piece of ice wasn't a true cube, it could not be called a cube—it could only be called a piece of ice.

Offhand, I couldn't think of any argument that would have interested me less.

As I was closing the incision, the gallery began to clear. And when I finished, the last resident had gone.

We sent Valerie to Recovery. Then Clover and I left the operating room.

"When you turn a boat into a hotel, you lose the whole purpose," he said. "If you want hotel living, why not go to a hotel?"

I didn't have any answer to that.

We began getting out of our surgical gear.

Clover laughed. "Sixteen hours on a sandbar," he said. "He wouldn't even wave." He tossed his gown at a refuse container. "Well, that's Frank Brice for you." Then he left.

That was all. No comment on the operation. If he had had some particular purpose in selecting me to do the job, he certainly hadn't revealed it. I was as much in the dark as ever.

I talked to Lou Manx again later.

"Maybe he's having second thoughts," he said. "Remember the Christmas party? Gar insisted that the fellowship was intended for a doctor going into practice. Maybe Clover's been thinking it over. Maybe he wanted to get a closer look at you."

I shook my head. "More likely he hoped I'd make a mistake, eliminate myself from the competition completely."

"I can't see Clover doing that."

"Isn't it possible? He'd be there to bail me out. And that gallery—why did he pass out invitations? So there'd be witnesses, if I slipped up?"

Lou squinted at me. "I don't think you know Clover very well," he said. "That isn't his kind of gimmick. He sent out invitations because he thought the operation was worth seeing. That's all. You're looking for a plot. But I say he picked you because he thought you were the best guy to handle the operation. Period."

126

That night, I tried out my theory on Sue.

"Oh, forgodsakes!" she said. "Do you know what your trouble is? You don't give yourself enough credit. Dr. Clover thought you could handle it, that's all. Why do you have to make something out of nothing? Do you know what your trouble is?"

"You just told me," I said.

"Besides that. When you were a child, did you go to a lot of movies?"

"How can I answer that? What is a *lot* of movies?"

"Everything is a Hollywood movie to you," she said. "Your attitude toward research. And now this— this whatever it is."

"Plot."

"Yes. Can't anything ever be simple?"

I said okay, she was probably right, I did over-dramatize. Then I changed the subject. And by the next day I had to admit Clover would never risk a patient's well-being just to show me up.

Along about the middle of April, Mrs. Cuckoo came back. She walked in out of nowhere and asked to be admitted. She had a severe cough and was having trouble breathing. X-rays showed that the tumor had spread to her lungs. She was admitted to a ward.

After the X-rays were taken, I was called in to consult, to determine whether there was any point in surgery. A look at the X-ray plates was enough to tell me. She was beyond help. In fact, she had been beyond help the first time she had come to Briggs.

I went to see her after seeing the plates. There was not a great deal left of her to look at. She was no longer plump. Her flesh was hanging on her now, and her cheeks were sunken. But she was still smiling.

She remembered me. "You're the Kipling fellow," she said when I stopped at her bed.

"Not exactly," I said. "Actually, you're the Kipling woman."

"Yes, that's what I meant."

"Why did you come back?" I asked. It was the question foremost in my mind.

"I remembered your raisin toast," she replied. "It was a Wednesday. I was sitting on a bench in the park, and I remembered, it being Wednesday, your raisin toast. Excellent raisin toast. The finest raisin toast I've ever had. I *will* say that for you. I don't much care for your beds—too hard. But you *do* make excellent raisin toast."

"What does Wednesday have to do with it?" I asked.

"It was on a Wednesday that I had your raisin toast, I remembered—sitting on the park bench. So, I said to myself, 'You really ought to have some more of that excellent raisin toast before you die.' That's why I came back."

I pulled up a chair and sat down beside the bed. I had never met a patient faced with death who seemed to be so indifferent to the fact.

"You should have come to us much sooner," I said. "You knew about the trouble, didn't you? Why didn't you see your doctor?"

She frowned, thinking. The question apparently had never occured to her.

Finally, she replied, "Well, I suppose it's because you weren't on my way."

"I don't understand."

"I didn't walk this way," she said. "I wasn't even in the neighborhood. I might have stopped in if I had been. But I just never got over this way until that day when I took a wrong bus."

"*That's* why you came in? You took a wrong bus?"

She frowned again. "As I recall it, yes, but I wouldn't stand on that. My memory isn't what it once was."

"Do you mind," I said, "if I ask you a few more questions?"

The bright smile returned to her face. "Oh, anything," she said. "My father used to say, 'If you don't ask questions, how will you ever find out?' Well, I suppose all fathers say that. But my father really meant it. But he always had an answer. Much better answers than the encyclopedia could offer. Not at all the *same* answers. Father and the encyclopedia were hardly ever in agreement. I remember the day that my sister Tulip asked him how many Punic Wars there were. 'Seven,' he replied, quick as a wink. Tulip didn't like the sound of the number, though—Tulip always claimed that seven was her unlucky number—so she went to look it up in the encyclopedia. A little later she came back and told Father that, according to the encyclopedia, there were only three. She was quite happy about it. Because three was her *lucky* number. Well, Father drew himself up and said, 'Tulip, if you choose to believe that there were only three Punic Wars, then that is your privilege. But,' he went on, 'keep in mind that since you weren't there to see for yourself, you are accepting someone else's word for it.'" She turned slightly away from me, her smile softening. "Dear, dear Father," she said. "He had such a way with explanations."

"He sounds . . . interesting," I said. That wasn't the word I had in mind.

"No, he was a very plain man. All he had, really, was his sense of what was fit. I like to think that I inherited that from him. Poor Tulip. All she got was

129

Father's plainness. She married early. To a man who was seven years her senior—although she didn't find that out until later. After they had separated." The smile faded. "She never forgave Father for having more Punic Wars than she had. She took it as a slight. Though, of course, Father meant it in the kindest way."

"Were you close to your Father?" I asked.

"Oh, no. I left the house early, too. Not to be married, though. I wanted to see where the bus went. There was a bus that passed our door. I always wondered where it went. So one day I got on it. I packed a dress and some underclothing, and taking nothing but that and Father's sense of fitness with me, got on the bus. I never went back." She turned back to me. "The bus went to Euclid Avenue," she said.

"This coming and going, in and out of the hospital, doing as you please, is that part of your sense of what is fit?" I asked.

"I assume so — if it's different," she replied. "I don't think about myself — or about what I do — so I can't truthfully answer the question. It may be the sense of what is fit. But on the other hand, I may be slightly insane. It's difficult to know."

"You don't worry much about things, do you?"

"I don't believe I do. That's another thing I don't think much about. But you may be right."

"Are you aware that your illness is very serious?"

Again, the thoughtful frown. "Yes, I've been told that."

"But it doesn't concern you. Why?"

"Well, my father used to say — every morning at breakfast — he used to say, 'Well, another day closer to the grave.' Tulip didn't like to hear that at all. She would ask him why he always said it, and why always

130

at breakfast. 'I say it because it's the truth,' he would reply. 'And I mention it at breakfast to get the matter over with for the rest of the day. That way, I don't have to think about it until the next morning. Never brood on death, Tulip.'"

"Is that why it doesn't concern you?"

"Probably. If I thought about it. But I don't."

We talked a little while longer, and then I left. I went back almost every day to see her. She did not linger long. She was on huge doses of cortisone, but the drug could only delay, not prevent.

She kept smiling — and talking — right to the end. She gave no sign of the pain.

Then one day when outside her room, I met two orderlies and a nurse wheeling her out on a stretcher. She had died a few minutes earlier.

I walked with them along the corridor as far as the elevator. I wanted to lift back the sheet and look at her. But I didn't dare. I was afraid that she might not still be smiling.

I never did understand her. I sometimes think about her now, later, and wonder whether she was saner than anyone realized.

Eleven

ALL OF A SUDDEN, hell broke loose for the surgical service. Until then — near the end of spring — we had had a fairly easygoing few months. There was time between cases, and we got out of the operating room at a decent hour.

131

But just as the warmer weather melted the snows, we found ourselves standing at the table all during the day and sometimes into the night. The fifth-year men got the brunt of it. Even Paul Brandt was called off his research. And Dr. Clover was seen more and more often in the operating rooms.

Dr. Gar loved it. He was infused with a new energy and enthusiasm. He even smiled occasionally, though he actually spent very little time at the table. He couldn't be wasted for that. He devoted himself to overseeing. The residents handled most of the cases, with Gar trotting from operating room to operating room, making sure that everything was proceeding according to his likes.

On top of that, a regional meeting of the College of Surgeons convened in a nearby hotel. And Dr. Mackey decided to show off the Briggs surgical service. As a result, we had surgeons from all over the area popping in on us, peeking over our shoulders, commenting — approvingly or snidely — as we worked. It didn't help much.

I hardly saw Sue and Peter. The instant I got home in the evening, my legs aching from standing such long hours, I would drop on the bed and sleep until around midnight. Then I would get up, eat something — I seldom knew exactly what it was I was eating — and then go back to bed until it was time to start the next day.

Sue was usually asleep — and remained asleep — when I got up at midnight. But every once in a while she would awaken and prepare my food and sit with me. Our conversations were pretty sterile, though. About all I could manage between swallows were grunts.

"Can't something be done about this?" she said one night.

"Uh."

"Somebody is going to make a mistake," she said. "A bad mistake. Somebody is going to kill somebody."

But it didn't happen. That was the miracle. It didn't happen, though one day, it came close.

I had just come off a case and was grabbing five minutes in the lounge when the phone rang. The operator said that a resident in Medicine wanted a surgical consult — he didn't care whom. So I took the call.

The resident, Bill Silver, came on and gave me a quick rundown. A male, white fifty-nine-year-old had come into the medical service two days earlier with mild stomach pain. Today, as he was on his way back from X-ray, he had suddenly gone into shock. Silver suspected blood loss, and confirmed his belief by a stat hematocrit — the red cell volume had dropped from the forty-four percent it had been at admission to thirty-six percent. However, no source for the bleeding could be found.

I told Silver to hang on to the X-rays and that I would be right down. When I got there, he was waiting for the plates to be developed.

Then the technician came in with another set of plates.

"These are the same guy," he said. "They were taken a couple months ago."

"He didn't tell me he was in here before," Silver said.

The technician shrugged. "Same guy," he insisted.

Silver looked at the information with the X-rays and said, yes, the man had been in before.

We put the old plates on the screen. After some squinting and sighing, we found what we thought

133

might be a large aneurism of the aorta — a weak spot in the main artery leading from the heart. We guessed that somewhere between the heart and the lower spine the aneurism had ruptured and there was a hole in the wall of the artery. That meant that there was no more time for speculation or examination. The man should have been on the table right then.

The resident ran to get the patient, and I got on the phone to arrange for an operating room. But every room was in use.

When I got back, Silver was giving the man an intravenous of whole blood.

"The operating rooms are all full," I told him. "But let's get him up there, anyway."

The resident held the bottle of whole blood, and I pushed the stretcher. We slammed out of the examining room and rushed down the corridor. Luckily, we had to wait only about five seconds for an elevator. I told the operator to express us to the surgical floor. Seconds later we emerged from the elevator and raced toward the nurses' station.

The nurse on duty told us the operating rooms were still in use.

"He can't wait," Silver said.

I pushed the stretcher through the double doors of the nearest operating room, then pulled up. We were in the short hallway that separated the actual operating room from the main corridor.

A nurse came out of the operating room.

"Get me an abdominal tray!" I snapped at her.

She started to say something.

"Don't talk — get!"

She rushed off.

I stripped the patient down. A moment later, the nurse came back with the tray. I snatched a scalpel and made a long midline incision from the end of the chest to the pubis. Then I opened him up wide. There was no time for technique.

Blood began spilling out of him. I reached in and pulled the entire bowel out through the incision. Our diagnosis was correct. The abdominal aorta had developed an aneurism which had ruptured. Blood was gushing out of the hole.

I put a Beck clamp on the aorta above the aneurism.

At that moment, I heard Dr. Clover's voice. "You're all right," he said. "Max is scrubbing. Get him into the operating room."

I hadn't been aware of Clover's arrival. Now I saw that I was almost surrounded by doctors.

Somebody pushed the stretcher away — into the operating room, which was now vacant and ready.

I followed the stretcher, and as we entered I saw Dr. Gar putting his arms through the sleeves of his robe.

"Scrub," he said to me. Then he went to the patient.

I scrubbed as quickly as I could.

When I got to the table, Gar was dissecting the second of the two iliac arteries, having already clamped the first. These were the arteries that branched from the aorta below the rupture. A Beck clamp had been placed on the first artery, and, as he finished with the second, I placed a clamp on it.

"Heparin," he said.

I injected 3cc of heparin into the arteries just below the clamps.

Gar stepped back, and I began clamping all of the smaller arteries that led from the aorta.

When I had finished, Gar moved in again. He cut the aorta just below the Beck clamp that I had put on in the hallway. Then, using scissors, he cut the aorta along the length of the damaged part. After that, he slipped a plastic tube into the area, and sewed it in place with 3-0 sutures.

Still sewing, Gar spoke to the anesthetist. "Are we all right up there?"

"You're in in a walk," he answered.

It was the first moment I had had to think about the patient. But he was apparently out of shock and very much alive.

When Gar finished the suturing, we got ready to remove the clamps. This was another danger point. The tremendous surge of blood into the lower extremities could cause the patient to go into shock again.

"You ready?" Gar said to the anesthetist, who would pump in the blood.

"Let 'er blow."

"Now!" Gar said.

At the same time, he removed the lower clamps, allowing blood to fill the arteries from below. And simultaneously he signaled to me. I removed the upper clamps near the heart. Speed was necessary here to keep the blood from forming a clot in the tube.

The patient took the blood well — no complications.

We waited a while, making sure that there was no leakage of blood from the suture line. Then — gently this time — we put the bowel back in place.

"You close," Gar said to me.

He left the table, and I began closing the incision.

Later, after the patient had been sent to Recovery, out of danger and breathing easily, I went back to the lounge.

As I dropped into a chair, Tris Maney came in. "Where the hell've you been?" he said "Mussleman is calling all over for you."

It hit me that I was overdue for a scrub with Dr.

Mussleman. I didn't stop to explain to Maney. I popped up out of the chair and ran for the scrub room.

I had three other scrubs that day. And it was eight at night before I was able to get off duty. I hadn't even had dinner.

When I was in the locker room, getting into my street clothes, Dr. Gar came in.

"Check the schedule before you leave," he said. "I've got a gastric resection at six in the morning, and I penciled you in on it."

That was all. He was just passing through. No comment on the man I had opened up in the hallway.

It seemed to me that somebody ought to say *something* about it. It was a bit of quick thinking and quick acting that had saved a man's life.

I checked the next morning's schedule, as Gar had ordered, then went home.

I told Sue about my big play that day. She, at least, appreciated it. She was willing to devote the whole evening to admiring me. But I remembered that I had to be at the table again at six the next morning. So I had half a beer and went to bed.

The breakneck pace continued for the next three weeks. Every day was the same. On weekends, I slept, trying to get back the energy I had lost during the week. Then, as abruptly as it had started, it stopped. Our case load fell off. I began getting home at a reasonable hour, and the ache left my legs.

It wasn't easy to slow down after running continuously for so long. Gar felt the change most. He turned up in the operating rooms eyeing our work even when his own patients weren't scheduled.

Then, about a week after things returned to normal, I got a call to see Dr. Clover. When I got to his desk, I found that he wasn't there, and I had to chase him down. He was in the research building.

I discovered that he had a real office there — not just a desk. It wasn't large, but it was well-furnished. And he seemed comfortable in it. I supposed that was because the office was in the research building, where, if he had had his way, he would have spent all his time.

He waved me into a chair. When I was seated, he said. "You handled that ruptured aneurism very well. I see that the patient is doing fine now. He can thank you for that."

I smiled weakly. I can never think of a reply to a compliment. I like compliments, approval, but damned if I can think of a graceful answer.

"I wish I could offer you a gold medal," he said. "But we seem to be fresh out. You'll have to make do with a pat on the back."

It occurred to me to say that I would settle for the fellowship. But of course I wasn't stupid enough to actually say it.

He turned his chair, so that he was facing slightly away from me, then he said, "I understand you're doing some research."

I hadn't expected that. "Not really," I said.

"Oh? Paul Brandt mentioned something."

"I *was* looking into a subject," I said, "but I dropped it."

"Why is that?"

"I didn't have the interest to follow it through," I said.

He nodded. "That happens." He got up and went to his window and stood with his back to me, looking out. "There's a lot of piddling around in research," he said. "A lot of wasted activity. Or, at least, it seems

138

that way. It's necessary, though. You find the right answer by discarding all the wrong answers."

"Yes, I understand that."

"Research doesn't get the recognition it deserves," he said. "All the glory goes to the man at the table."

"Well . . ."

"People — most people — don't stop to think that the techniques that are used by the practicing surgeon were worked out — most of the time — in a lab." He faced back toward me, but remained at the window. "That ruptured aneurism," he said. "That plastic tube that went into that artery. That was worked out through research. You — you and Max — standing at the table, you saved the patient's life. But who made it possible for you to do it?"

I nodded.

"Not many people think about that," he said, moving back to his chair.

"Yes, sir," I said. "But, on the other hand, without somebody to stand at the table, the research would be worthless. Somebody has to take it and use it."

He smiled. "That has already been pointed out to me, thank you. A number of times. Most recently by Dr. Gar."

"I just meant that both are important — research and practice."

"Yes, I understand what you meant. My point is that the man at the table usually gets the recognition. I think it's about time research got its share of the glory."

What he was telling me, I guessed, was that the fellowship would go to Brandt.

"I wouldn't want to take anything away from research," I said. I said it with heavy and obvious insincerity.

"Good. I'm glad you think that way," Clover replied. He told me again what a good job I had done on the ruptured aneurism. And that ended the interview.

It did accomplish one thing. It killed the last hope I had of getting the fellowship.

The disappointment weighed pretty heavily on me for a few days. I came down with a fever, which might have been diagnosed as psychosomatic. At any rate, it kept me away from the hospital, at home in bed, for seventy-two hours. My case wasn't severe enough to get me admitted to the hospital.

While at home, I groused most of the time, grumbling, complaining. Sue brought me my meals and my medicine and kept Peter out of the bedroom and, in general, tried to boost my spirits. I had told her about my talk with Clover, and she probably knew what my real trouble was.

By the night of the third day, I was in a truly hairy mood. I was snapping at Sue, bitching about the food, about my confinement, about anything and everything within sight or earshot. Peter cried out for some reason in the hallway, and I leaped out of bed, flung open the door, and screamed bloody murder at him.

A few minutes later, my door opened, and Sue came in. She lit into me for screaming at Peter — it seemed that he had stepped on his own finger and thus had a good reason for crying out. In response, I began screaming at her.

It was a fairly good fight, as fights go. At the end of it, Sue was sobbing, and I was feeling fine, completely cured. I apologized to her. She forgave me. She called Peter in. He forgave me — although, by then, he had forgotten that I had screamed at him and didn't know what he was forgiving me for.

Later, after Peter was asleep, Sue and I talked out the matter of the fellowship. We decided that not getting it did not mean that life had come to an end. We started thinking about the future. I had had some offers to go into practice as a junior partner, and we began comparing the positions, taking the first steps toward making a decision. The crisis, it seemed, had passed, and we had survived.

When I returned to the hospital the next day, however, I found that the crisis there hadn't passed — it was just starting. Somehow, I discovered, it had become general knowledge that Clover intended to award the fellowship to a researcher. It may have been that Clover himself leaked the word. No official decision had been made, but it was assumed that the official announcement, when it came, would be a mere formality. Oddly enough, in all the discussion that followed, it was always said that the fellowship would go to "a researcher." Everyone knew that, in fact, they meant Paul Brandt, but no one used Paul's name. It was always "a researcher." I didn't understand why this was — and I still don't understand it. I simply report it.

Rumors greeted me on my first day back. I was not on the morning schedule, since they hadn't known I was better, so I got some books from the library, took them to the lounge, and settled down for a morning's reading.

Not long after that, George Bruner came in, just off a scrub. "You here?" he said. "I thought you'd headed for the hills."

"Don't kid me," I said. "I don't do anything that you don't know about. Sue tells Marge, and Marge tells you. I'll bet you even know it every time I go to the john." Then I closed my book. "Why the hills?"

141

"Gar and Clover," he replied. "Haven't you heard?"

I told him no.

"The way I understand it," he said, "Clover has decided to give the fellowship to a research man. I guess that doesn't surprise you."

"I don't know," I said "Ask Marge. She'll know whether it surprises me or not."

"She says you know."

"I've got an idea that's the way it'll go," I said.

"Then you've got an idea, I guess, how Gar is taking it."

I shook my head.

"Not without a fight, evidently," George said. "The way I hear it, he's rounding up support, putting the pressure on Clover."

"Support from whom?"

"Everybody he can lay a hand on. Subtle, you know, but doing it. He's insisting the fellowship is meant for a guy who's going into practice."

"That's not new."

"But he's stomping down hard, trying to make Clover change his mind. All the surgeons, I guess, are helping. You know how they do, they run into Clover, accidentally, then put the pitch to him."

"It's Clover's decision to make," I said.

"Sure. But he's only human, isn't he? With everybody against it, he's going to stop and think."

I shook my head. "Not Clover. I don't think he'd ever buckle under to that kind of pressure. I wouldn't myself — not if I were him. Either he's head of the section or he's not. If he is — and, dammit, *he is* — he has to call the shots the way he sees them. Especially on a thing like this. It isn't medicine, it's politics."

"Call it whatever you want," George said. "At least Gar's taking care of his own. You have to hand it to the son-of-a-bitch."

A few days later, I got another opinion. This time from Lou Manx.

"If you want my advice," he said, "you'll stay out of it. I told Paul the same thing. Make out like you don't even know it's going on."

"I intend to," I said. "But I'm tempted, tempted to say something to Gar, that is."

"Stay clear," Lou said. "I know, George is going around leading the cheer for Gar, but there's more to it than that. I think Gar's riding his own horse, not yours."

"Meaning what?"

"Think about it. Gar is as good a man as Clover. His prestige is as high. And he expected he'd get Clover's job. Don't think he wouldn't like to chop Clover down a couple inches. My guess is that he wants to — consciously or unconsciously — and he's making his play."

"Using this fellowship as a lever, you mean?"

"Right. He's got the weight with him. The surgeons are going to back him up. They don't want to see a research man get that fellowship. It's a dig at them — they *think*. So they'll continue putting the presssure on Clover."

"How will that help Gar?" I asked.

"If the pressure works, if Clover backs down, Gar will be the guy who backed him down. It'll mean something. For the moment, maybe, only a nibble of revenge, but, in the long run, a start on easing Clover out."

"If that's the way it really is," I said, "then Gar is actually hurting my chances for the fellowship, not helping. Putting on pressure will make Clover dig in and stick to his decision."

"That's my point," Lou said, "I don't think Gar

143

hopes to gain anything for you by forcing the issue. But no matter how it works out, Gar can't lose. If Clover sticks — which he probably will — then he'll have the surgeons pissed off at him. And Clover needs them on his side. He can't stay in as head of the section with his whole staff bucking him."

"Okay, but suppose he gives in?"

"Then he's lost face."

"Maybe."

"Maybe hell. Gar has Clover in a corner. And the beauty of it is, Clover put himself there. That fellowship has always gone to a guy who intended to practice. If Clover hadn't tried to change things, he'd be home free right now."

"It stinks a little, doesn't it?" I said.

Lou grinned. "It stinks good," he said. "I haven't enjoyed anything as much in years." He pointed a finger at me. "Just remember — stay clear of it."

"I'm not going to do a thing," I assured him. "It's Clover's monkey, let him carry it."

If I could, I would now take that comment back. It wasn't very kind.

Twelve

THE FOLLOWING day, something happened that seemed innocent enough at the time. It wasn't until almost two weeks later that I realized that there was a special purpose behind it.

I got a call to report to Dr. Alex Andeleu in one of the examining rooms in surgery. When I got there, he had a patient on the table. He ignored me — I simply stood there, looking dumb — until he finished and the patient, a man, was wheeled away. Then he motioned me to follow him into the small office off the examining room.

Dr. Andeleu was a big man in kidneys. He was a short, bandy-legged, tough little bird. He talked out of the side of his mouth in machine-gun bursts.

When we reached the office, he handed me a history and physical.

"Read."

I read. It was on a Ralph Tobin. He had a diseased kidney. He had been kept alive on a special diet (limiting his intake of fluids and salt) and drugs.

"As it stands, he has two months," Andeleu said. "He needs a new kidney."

I nodded. That was obvious.

"I have a donor," Andeleu said. "He's willing to part with a kidney — a *healthy* kidney. I'm going to do a transplant." He handed me a slip of paper from the desk. "This is a list of papers on kidney transplants," he said. "Get them. Read them. When you finish, give me a call. You have two days. Then you and I will talk out the operation. We'll operate on Friday. I want you to assist me."

He walked out.

I was somewhat surprised. Dr. Andeleu had never shown any particular interest in me before. But I was more pleased than surprised. Kidney transplants didn't occur very often, and it was one hell of an opportunity to be in on one.

I got the papers from the library and read them through thoroughly, several times. A number of the papers were by Dr. Andeleu himself. He was recognized as one of the top men in his specialty.

We met again on Thursday afternoon. He had me

describe the operation step by step. I made some mistakes in the first run-through. He looked pained. In fact, I got the impression that he would have liked to forget the whole thing. That probably should have told me that this opportunity he was giving me wasn't as innocent as it appeared. Anyway, I talked the operation a second time. This time I made only one error. He seemed mildly relieved. But he made me go through it again — from beginning to finish — and, on the third try, I got it completely right.

"We're scheduled for ten o'clock," he said, getting up. "Be ready at eight."

I got to the hospital at seven-thirty the next morning. I checked the schedule first, and saw that the operation was to be done in the main operating room. That probably meant a gallery again. Then I went down to the cafeteria to get a cup of coffee.

Dr. Andeleu was there, so instead of going upstairs, we sat in the cafeteria and went over the operation there. A little after nine, he left to see the patient, and I went up to scrub.

He arrived while I was still at the sink. He stepped up next to me and began scrubbing, without saying anything. We stood side by side for about a quarter of an hour without communicating. His silence here, I assumed, was habitual. He wasn't a pleasant man.

When we got to the operating room, it looked like Times Square. Dr. Andeleu had apparently called everybody he could think of, to have plenty of personnel at hand in case of an emergency. The gallery, too, was pretty well filled.

Everyone responsible for any sort of machine wheeled it into place, to be ready. And the patient was there, on the table, being fussed over by the scrub nurse.

Andeleu looked at the clock. Timing was important in this. While we were opening our patient, another team of surgeons in another operating room would be removing the healthy kidney from the donor.

Andeleu went around to each of the people in the operating room, making sure they knew their responsibilities and were prepared. I followed him along this route, learning.

Then, after looking at the clock again, he gave the go-ahead to the anesthetist. It was the beginning of what was to be a three-hour-and-fifty-six-minute operation.

Andeleu made the first incision, a thin line that marked the limits. He certainly had a delicate touch. Only a hint of blood seeped out.

Then he went deeper. I moved in with the retractors.

He went deeper.

"Clamps."

I began clamping.

Andeleu bent over. He seemed almost to put his head into the hole. Then, pulling back slightly, he separated the kidney from its bed.

My mind moved ahead to the next step, so that I could anticipate my own duties.

In fifteen minutes, he was ready to remove the diseased organ. It actually looked sick. It was pale, a grayish color.

When the kidney was free, the circulating nurse moved in, took it from Andeleu, and carted it away. Then I began preparing the resting place for the healthy kidney. The plan was to place it in the lower abdomen near the hipbone.

The timing was off by a minute or so. The patient was ready but the healthy kidney hadn't arrived.

Andeleu started swearing. Dr. Morris, the surgeon who was supplying the healthy kidney, was a flub-footed incompetent. His scrub nurse was a flea-brained bitch. The whole hospital was staffed from the ground floor to top floor with half-assed idiots.

The rest of us simply listened.

Then the healthy kidney arrived, carried in a basin by a circulating nurse.

Andeleu's anger subsided. He was all business again.

He injected an anticoagulant into the vessels of the donated kidney. The purpose of this was to try to keep clots from forming.

Then carefully, he nestled the kidney into the "bed" we had prepared for it.

"What next?" he said to me.

I replied. It was the right answer.

He signaled to me to proceed. And, working as quickly as I could, I began suturing the kidney vein to the iliac vein.

Andeleu watched me, making guttural sounds that might have meant anything. But he didn't interfere — or say anything that was understandable — so I assumed that I was passing the test.

When I had finished, he signaled to me again. I began suturing the renal and hypogastric arteries.

Apparently I wasn't working fast enough to suit him.

"I'd like to finish this before Sunday," he snapped at me.

I nodded, picking up the pace.

I got the feeling after a few more minutes that he wanted to take the job out of my hands. But that may have been a result of my own nervousness. In any case, when I had finished connecting the arteries, he again signaled me to proceed, and I began suturing the ureter to the bladder.

I was beginning to tire. Sweat was pouring down my face. The circulating nurse was daubing at my forehead every few minutes. The calves of my legs felt as if they were being stuck with pins.

But Andeleu had started to enjoy himself. Perhaps because my weariness was showing. His guttural growl became a low, musical hum.

When I finished, he waved me back, without looking directly at me. I accepted this as a compliment. If I hadn't pleased him, I was sure he would have been swearing.

"Watch your goddamn gauges up there," he said to the anesthetist.

Then he began releasing the clamps.

Blood flowed into the transplanted kidney. He bent over, nearly touching the incision. After a few seconds he straightened. The sutures were tight; there was no leakage.

"Well, now it's in the lap of the gods — whoever the goddamn hell *that* might be," he said. He signaled to me again. "Let's close."

I began the closing, not knowing whether the operation was a success or failure. It was impossible to know at that point. The transplant might or might not take. It would be months before we could even begin to hope with any assurance.

Dr. Andeleu offered no comment on my work — which was, in his case, I suppose, a comment in itself. But a number of residents spoke to me about it. And even Dr. Gar mentioned it. This was surprising. He had never said anything to me about any operations I had done with him.

However, at the time, I simply accepted the compliments. I didn't ask myself whether anything unusual was going on.

Two days later, I was summoned by Dr. Richard Maltus, a neurosurgeon. Maltus was fairly young, in his early forties. He was a stringbean of a man, with a thatch of blond hair that sat on top of his head like a shock of yellow wheat. He was easygoing, relaxed, and soft-spoken.

When he called me, he asked me to meet him in the main waiting room. Puzzled, I went there, and then he suggested that we go out to a small restaurant near the hospital for a cup of coffee.

Seated at a table, he told me that he had an operation scheduled for next Monday and he wanted me to assist. My puzzlement soared. He had plenty of residents who were specializing in neurosurgery to assist him. Why pick me?

I didn't ask, of course. And he didn't volunteer an explanation.

He began talking about the case. It was a Parkinson, a disease in which the patient suffers from perpetual tremor. In its advanced stage, it renders the patient almost completely rigid. The cause of the disease isn't yet known. But some of the symptoms can be treated. Dr. Maltus explained that he was using a new technique that involved shooting liquid nitrogen into the brain to destroy the area that was causing the tremors.

I told him frankly that I didn't think I was qualified to assist him.

"Maybe 'assist' is too strong," he said. "But I thought you might like to be there at the table. It could be a valuable experience."

I thanked him for the opportunity. Then he told me to get in touch with one of his residents, Art Lee, whom I knew. He said that Lee would brief me on the operation.

Lee was a Chinese-American, round-faced and always smiling. I looked him up that afternoon. Dr. Maltus told him that I would be in to see him.

"You switching to neurosurgery?" he asked.

I said no.

His smile disappeared for a second, and he looked perplexed. Then he shrugged and began telling me how the operation was performed.

The following Monday, at nine in the morning, I appeared in the scrub room as scheduled. When I got there, Maltus and Lee were already finished and gowned. Again the main operating room was being used. I was getting so used to having a gallery that I wondered if I would ever be able to work again without one.

When I went inside, I saw Maltus and Lee standing by the door talking. The patient hadn't arrived yet, but nurses and interns were buzzing about, making preparations. I joined Maltus and Lee.

They were discussing, for godsakes, mushrooms. That is, Maltus was talking about mushrooms and Lee was listening. Maltus amiably tried to draw me into the conversation, but all I knew about mushrooms was that I could take them or leave them alone. What I learned was that he was an amateur mushroom grower, and that he grew them in manure. That was probably enough to know.

After a while, the patient was wheeled in and we went to the table. The gallery was filling up by then. Scouting the crowd, I saw Lou Manx come in.

The patient was a man of about fifty. He was conscious, though not completely. Conscious enough, however, to hear and to speak.

"Well, let's see now," Maltus said, smiling at the man. "Raise your arm for me."

The man complied. His hand shook as if it were wired to a vibrator.

"Down," Maltus said.

The arm was lowered.

"I'm sure glad you're not operating on me," Maltus grinned.

A low chuckle came from the man.

We stepped back from the table, and the nurses continued the preparations.

An anesthetist came in. Maltus called across to him. "Easy day for you!"

The anesthetist joined us. "I didn't get breakfast," he said. "Do you mind if I send out for some oatmeal?"

That got a big laugh — from the anesthetist.

Finally we began.

The patient's head had been shaved. Maltus did some measuring and calculating, then made a mark on the skull. After that, the anesthetist injected a local anesthetic.

"Well, anyone have any objections?" Maltus smiled.

Lee chuckled.

"Scalpel."

The scrub nurse put the scalpel into his hand. He made a small incision.

I looked at the patient's face. It was passive. He seemed to be thinking about something far away in the past.

"Drill."

The scrub nurse passed the drill. Maltus began boring a hole in the skull where he had made the incision. The drill whined.

Behind us, a cryosurgery unit was being brought up. It was a boxlike apparatus, with dials and a measure graph on its face. It contained a tank of pressurized liquid nitrogen, which was kept at −352.8°F. Attached to the machine was a tube and nozzle apparatus.

The technician passed the tube to Lee, who waited with it.

Maltus eased the drill from the hole he had made in the skull. As he did so, I saw that his manner had changed. He no longer looked relaxed. There was a grimness about his mouth, and his eyes had become dead serious. I don't think at that point anyone would have dared joke about sending out for oatmeal.

The scrub nurse took the drill. Maltus kept his hand extended, and she next put a double-bow-like device into it. The device conformed to the shape of the skull. It was a guide to be used for positioning the cannula, the needle that would be inserted through the hole in the skull.

"All right, let's go," Maltus said sharply to Lee.

The scrub nurse passed the cannula to Lee and he fitted it to the nozzle which, in turn, was fitted to the tube connected to the cryosurgery unit.

When the cannula was attached, Lee passed it to Maltus.

Then, so slowly that I had trouble discerning the movement, Maltus began inserting the cannula into the brain, aiming for the thalmus.

Time dragged. I became aware of my own breathing. It was fairly steady — but, as I paid more attention to it, it increased. That interested me, the fact that when I concentrated on my breathing, the pace increased. I thought about it for a while. There was nothing else to do.

Finally, after what seemed like hours, Maltus straightened up and checked the position of the needle by X-ray. He was right on the target.

But he made another test to be absolutely sure. A minor amount of liquid nitrogen was pumped to the tip of the cannula to cool the thalmus.

Then he spoke to the patient. "Raise that arm again."

There was a pause — almost a theatrical pause. Then slowly the arm raised. The hand was no longer shaking.

Maltus permitted himself a small smile. Then, "Down," he ordered.

The arm lowered.

Maltus spoke to the man at the cryosurgery unit. "30 p.s.i.," he said.

There was a nod, and the man repeated the order for pressure. "30 p.s.i."

Maltus turned his attention back to the cannula. He gave the signal. Frigid liquid nitrogen was pumped into the thalmus, destroying a portion of it.

Then Maltus began withdrawing the needle.

When it was out, Lee stepped into place to take over the closing.

I continued to stand, watching. I had done absolutely nothing but stand and watch. I had learned something, of course, but I doubted that Maltus was that interested in my pursuit of knowledge. So why had he asked me to be there?

I talked to Sue about it that night.

"They're finally beginning to appreciate you," she said.

"Bull. Maltus doesn't know one damn thing about me. I'm surprised he even knew my name.

"Maybe he wanted to interest you in neurosurgery."

"Bull again. He didn't mention it. He didn't even ask if I might be remotely interested." I shook my head. "No, I suspect that Maltus has no intention of ever seeing me again."

"Maybe he just likes to have somebody new around occasionally to talk to about mushrooms," she suggested.

That made about as much sense as any other idea.

The following day I found a note in my box from Dr. Clarence Leki. The signature was scribbled and I wasn't sure of it, so I checked it with the attendant at the desk. She confirmed that it was Leki's writing.

Surprises were beginning to pile up. Dr. Leki liked to pretend that residents, no matter how senior, didn't exist. He was a hard-nosed old coot, with more talent than any one man should be allotted. He didn't want any surgeon standing at the table with him who hadn't had several years in practice. When he operated, he was assisted by one or more of the junior men in his office, never by a hospital resident.

It was two days before I got in touch with him. When I called his office, his nurse told me that he had no time at the moment to talk to me and advised me to call later. I called four times after that, and got the same answer. Then on the second day he suddenly appeared in the scrub room when I was preparing for another case.

He told me that he had a radical mastectomy scheduled the following week and that he wanted me to assist him. All I could offer in response was a dumb stare. That apparently suited him; he turned and walked out.

It was all getting to be a bit too much. I had to talk to someone besides Sue about it. So, later that day, I got Lou Manx alone and told him what had been happening.

When I mentioned Leki, he said, "Jesus God, don't

you know what that means? He's going to invite you in with him."

I said bull to him, too.

"Then what else?"

"Crank up your antenna," I said. "You tell me."

We were in the cafeteria, sitting at a table. He leaned back in his chair and stuck his long legs out into the aisle. He pondered for a moment in silence, then he said, "Damned if I know."

"First Andeleu," I said, "and then Maltus, and now Leki. Does that make sense to you?"

He shook his head. "I saw you with Maltus," he said. "That was a damn good job you did."

"What do you mean? I didn't do a blessed thing."

"You stayed on your feet, didn't you? And good, too. The best job of standing I've seen in a long time."

"All right, that's exactly what I mean. Why did he have me in there?"

"Did he say anything?"

"Like what?"

"I don't know. What did he talk about?"

"He told me about his friggin' mushrooms."

Lou made a face. "That's it," he said. "He's going to set you up with a mushroom garden. He's probably thinking of a whole chain of mushroom gardens. And he's recruiting residents to take over the franchises. That's a logical thought. I've seen a lot of residents who were cut out for just that — mushroom gardening. They were sure as hell out of their depth in medicine."

"Your antenna is bent."

"No, I'm picking *some*thing up. You know what I think? I'll bet Gar is mixed up in this."

"How? Why?"

"I don't know. I'll think about it."

Thirteen

THE DAY before Leki's operation, I got a call from one of the junior surgeons in his office, a Dr. James Willet. He told me he would be at the hospital that day and that he wanted a few minutes with me. Later, in the afternoon, I got a summons over the loudspeaker, and when I picked up the phone the operator connected me with Willet. He was at one of the nurses' stations and asked me to meet him there.

When I reached the floor, he took me into the tiny office behind the station. He was a hard young guy; about thirty-five, I guessed. He wore rimless glasses, and his eyes, behind the lenses, looked like two cold round stones.

But his manner was warm enough — even though I did suspect that he was trying a bit too hard. He talked to me about the operation.

"You have assisted at a breast removal before, haven't you?" he said.

I nodded. If he knew anything about me — and he apparently did — he knew that.

"The operation is scheduled for the main operating room," he said. "That won't bother you, will it? The gallery, I mean."

"It's my second home," I said.

Then he told me that Leki intended to take the operation a step further than the usual radical mastectomy. A cluster of lymph nodes near the sternum sometimes serves as a sort of well for cancer cells, and, in this case, he intended to remove the section of the chest in which these cells were imbedded. The result would be a kind of window in the center of the chest. And this, of course, would mean that he would have to build up a support to take the place of the bone that had been removed.

I had heard about the technique. Leki used it more than any other doctor at Briggs, and in that limited sphere it had become his trademark.

"There's one other thing," Willet said. He turned slightly away from me. "The fact that Dr. Leki has asked you to assist him on — Let me phrase that another way. The fact that Dr. Leki has offered you the opportunity to observe and participate in this operation does not imply any particular commitment on his part."

I didn't know what the hell he was getting at. I looked dumb, I suppose.

"What I mean is," he said, "Dr. Leki's office is completely staffed as it is."

That was clear enough. The fact that Leki had "offered me the opportunity to observe and participate" did not mean that he was considering asking me into his harem. Fair enough. I hadn't wanted in. But why, then, had he asked me to "observe and participate?"

When I got to the scrub room on the morning of the operation, Dr. Leki and Willet were at the sinks. Willet said hello to me, but Leki didn't even give me a grunt. I felt like an intruder.

When we got to the operating room, everybody involved in the operation, including the patient, was already there. The patient was fifty-four years old. I'd learned that from the history and physical. All I saw of her in the operating room was her chest area.

There was only a sprinkling of interns and residents in the gallery. The fact was, the operation didn't really belong in the main operating room. It didn't require all the facilities and was too routine to attract an audience. We were there, apparently, on Leki's whim.

Leki got right down to business. He stepped up to the table, then told me where to stand—at the side of Willet. That told me one thing—it was Willet who was actually going to assist. If I did *any* participating, it would be damn little. It looked to me like another morning of standing.

Leki was a fast man. He proceeded with the breast removal, bing, bing, bing, making his elliptical incision, then removing the mammary lymph nodes near the armpit and collarbone, as if he were at a meat counter slicing liver. Not that he was crude about it. It was just that he had the technique down pat. He knew what he was doing, and he did it, with no extra motion and no delay.

Then he slowed down a bit. He began pulling back the skin and outer tissue of the chest.

"Hemostats."

Willet stepped aside and motioned to me.

I took his place and began applying the hemostats to cut the flow of blood. It wasn't *much* to do, but it was something.

When Leki had the breastbone exposed, Willet eased me out and took the mallet and chisel from the scrub nurse. He began chipping away at the breastbone.

While Willet was at work, Leki glanced up at the

gallery. He looked neither pleased nor displeased, but I got the impression that he would have been happier if everyone had gone away.

When Willet had cut through the breastbone, Leki put a finger through the opening, feeling for the spot where he would chip through to make the larger aperture. Then the chiseling began again, Leki doing it this time.

Finally, the opening was complete. A tube was put into the hole to collect the fluids. Then Leki began cutting out the lymph nodes.

I stood. Time dragged. The gallery became smaller. The only sounds were Leki's requests for instruments. Leki straightened up. Willet began cutting out the lymph nodes. Still I stood.

When the nodes had been removed, Leki began sewing a kind of latticework of sutures across the opening. It was a slow, tedious job. When that was finished, Willet sutured in a covering of connective tissue (animal fascia). They were both good at it. When they were through, the covering had a strong, taut look. I *did* learn.

The closing, too, was a laborious job. It was more than an hour before we left the operating room. Leki stripped out of his gear without saying a word to either Willet or me. Then he steamed off:

"He's a bundle of laughs, isn't he?" I said.

"There are compensations," Willet said. Then he, too, departed.

I supposed there were compensations. But there weren't for me. I wished that Leki had planned to tap me for his office. It would have been a small pleasure to say no to him.

I had two more operations that day. They came one right after the other, so I didn't have much time to think about my experience with Dr. Leki. That night, however, I did get an answer. Whether it was the right one or not, I am still not sure.

After my final scrub, I went into the small lounge off the dressing room. Lou Manx and George Bruner were there. They were debating the superiorities and inferiorities of the Cubs and the White Sox.

Lou Manx broke off the conversation to say to me, "I saw you with Leki this morning."

"Was I brilliant?"

"Magnifico, baby. You handled those hemostats like a veteran—War of 1812."

"Every time I go into the main operating room, I see you," George said. "What do you do, sleep in there?"

"Stand, yes. Sleep, no," I replied. "But catch me next week. I'm going to do my nodding act. I'm working up to sleep."

"What's Sue giving you for dinner tonight?" Lou said.

"Who knows? We have a deal. I don't ask her what she feeds me, and she doesn't do any neurosurgery."

"I'll risk it, anyway," Lou said. "Shall I call her and tell her she invited me?"

"Somebody better."

I called her. And that evening when I checked out, Lou Manx joined me on the trek across the street to the apartment building.

Sue, who didn't have a great deal of faith in her cooking, had decided that we would send out for pizza. So we—the three of us in the living room—started out with beers and potato chips and a dip that Sue had whipped up.

When we were half through the first beer, Lou

said, "I've put my antennae to work. I think I see where Gar fits into the act."

Sue and I leaned forward.

"Let's see what we have," Lou said. "Over the past couple weeks, three of the big guns have called you in on operations. Right? The question is—why?"

"That part we know," I said.

"Okay. Now, we also have this thing between Gar and Clover. We have Gar talking to the surgeons, getting them to pressure Clover to stick to the intent of that fellowship. Right?"

"That's what *you* say," I said. "We don't have any proof. It's just an idea. Your idea."

"But it's logical—right?"

"*I* think it is," Sue said.

"It's still just an idea," I insisted.

"Grant me this," Lou said. "Grant me that it's possible."

"Granted."

"Okay, now. Maybe Gar wants to push things a little bit further. Maybe he wants to make you look like the fair-haired boy. How would he do it?"

"Hang up some arrows pointing to me? 'Fair-haired Boy'?"

"Put you in the spotlight," Lou said.

"You mean in the main operating room."

"Exactly. In the main operating room. Working with the big guns."

"Bull," I said.

He leaned back. "Then *you* tell *me* why."

I couldn't.

"I think Lou is right," Sue said. "It *would* make it more difficult for Dr. Clover. Wouldn't it? There you are, big as life, standing at the table with all of the top surgeons. It would make people think, wouldn't it?"

"I just can't see Gar and these guys in a conspiracy like that," I said. "My God, this isn't a spy drama, it's a hospital."

"Hell," Lou said, "I'm not saying they got together in a back room and figured this out. All I'm saying is that it could have evolved—naturally. One guy might have said, 'Okay, I think I'll take a look at this guy — see how good he is. I'll have him assist on an operation.' And another guy could have figured, okay, that's not a bad idea, I'll do the same thing. See what I mean?"

"I agree with Lou," Sue said. She turned back to me. "Don't you see it?"

"Yeah, yeah, yeah, I see it." I didn't *want* to see it—but I *did* see it.

"You have to admit—it'll make it tougher on Clover," Lou said. "Before, there wasn't a lot of talk about the fellowship award. But now, Gar has people speculating, taking sides. And that is going to make it a hell of a lot tougher. Here you've got a fair-haired boy, a guy who deserves the fellowship. And Clover is trying to turn thumbs down on the guy. It isn't going to make him look too good—not with the surgeons, anyway."

I got up and ordered the pizza. I didn't care to hear any more about it.

Lou left a little after midnight. In the meantime, we had talked about other things, but once Lou was gone, Sue picked up the thread again.

"It can't hurt you," she said. "All it can do is help you. If the pressure gets strong enough, Dr. Clover may change his mind. He may *have* to give you the fellowship."

"For the wrong reason," I said.

"But you deserve the fellowship. The only reason you're not getting it is because Dr. Clover is playing favorites."

"We didn't kick about that when Gar was running the show," I said. "When *I* was the favorite, we didn't do any screaming."

"We're *not* screaming," she said. "We're just acknowledging some facts, that's all."

"The damn thing just stinks," I said. "They talk about the intent of the fellowship. But, goddammit, the intent wasn't to use it as a political football. Nobody's really thinking about the real purpose any more. The question is, who will win? Not me or Paul. Gar or Clover."

"Well, honey, that's the way life is sometimes. People are people. I don't think you can change that. Not before it's time to award the fellowship, anyway."

"That doesn't take the stink off it."

"Well . . . You don't know what Dr. Clover will do. Maybe he'll stick to his guns, and that will be that. Would *that* make you happier? To lose?"

"In this case, maybe it would," I said.

"Then why don't you go to Dr. Gar and tell him to stop?"

"I can't. I don't have any proof that he's doing anything. What can I say? Tell the top surgeons not to schedule me with them any more? That'd be great. I'd sound like the Ass of the Year. You heard what Lou said—it isn't a plan."

"Couldn't you hint?"

"The only thing I can think of is, 'If you and Clover want to cut each other's throats, leave me out of it.' How's that?"

"Then what can you do?"

"Nothing."

As it happened, nothing was the right thing to do. Not long afterwards, the matter worked itself out, with an unintended assist from Albert Mieslau.

Mieslau was thirty-five, the father of six children. As a child himself he had had rheumatic fever, and the illness had damaged his heart. Mieslau had been a patient of Dr. Arn Jorgeson's for about ten years. Despite digitalis and diuretic medicine, the only thing that was really keeping him on his feet was guts.

I had been in twice to consult on the case. Each time, surgery had been recommended. But Mieslau had decided against it. He had great faith in the idea that if he hung on hard enough, nothing could shake him loose from life.

But apparently his faith was beginning to weaken. Or perhaps horse sense was taking its place. Whatever the reason, he had decided to gamble, to have open heart surgery to replace his diseased heart valve.

It was a complicated operation. The mortality rate was as high as twenty percent. But, without surgery, he would probably live only a few more years, and be inactive at that.

Because I had followed the case before, I was called in when Mieslau came into the hospital this time. He looked bad. His neck veins were distended, a sign of heart failure. His heart was so enlarged that each beat was clearly visible against his chest. He had a loud, blowing diastolic murmur, and his liver was enlarged and his ankles swollen, the latter two other signs of heart failure. A cardiac catheterization showed that his aortic valve was leaking.

Dr. Jorgeson asked Dr. Clover to take a look at the case. I was there when Clover made his examination. And I was present, too, when Clover told Mieslau that surgery was essential and what his chances were to come out of it alive. Mieslau made up his mind on the spot.

"Cut," he said disgustedly. "I'd be better off dead than the way I am now."

I assumed that I would be scrubbing on the case. But when the schedule was posted, Paul Brandt's name was on it. He would assist Clover.

And it wasn't long before the wheels in the rumor mill began turning.

Lou Manx's antennae quivered. "This is where Clover knocks them right out of the box," he said. All the surgeons have left is a whimper. He's got them — they're dead."

"How?" I said wearily.

"He's putting Paul in there for a grandstand play." Lou smiled. "These surgeons have been talking practice — okay, he's going to show them a practicing surgeon. This is a complicated operation, right? He's holding it in the big tent, right?"

"The where?"

"The main operating room. You know the place — your second home. He's holding it in the big tent, and he'll probably pass out personal invites, and he'll hand Paul the ball and say, 'Go, boy, go!'"

"You're playing a football game in a circus tent," I said.

"It won't be the first time."

I shook my head. "I thought I ought to be assisting on this, but then, the more I thought about it, the more logical it seemed to have Paul. It's a heart valve job. Paul is doing research on heart valves. It's reasonable."

Lou grinned. "You're okay as a surgeon," he said, "but you don't know one damn thing about show biz. I say Clover is setting Paul up to star. You watch.

166

When they get into that operating room, he'll give Paul the lead role. And Paul will pull it off — he'll do a slick, clean job — and what can the surgeons say after that?"

That night when I told Sue Lou's new theory, she replied, "Bull."

I laughed. "Me, too."

In spite of what I thought — or didn't think — I went to the main operating room the morning the operation was scheduled. I had just taken a seat in the gallery when Lou Manx came in. He plopped down beside me. About two-dozen other interns and residents had already assembled.

"How does it feel to be present at your own funeral?" Lou grinned.

"I don't believe it," I said.

Most of the participants were already in the pit — the scrub nurse, the circulating nurse, the nurse who was operating the bypass machine, an intern, a couple of third-year residents, the anesthetist. They were prepping, moving about the room — all except the anesthetist — gliding past each other, saying nothing, performing the routine.

Then the patient, Albert Mieslau, was wheeled in. I saw him turn his head to one side — apparently he wasn't quite out.

The nurses moved in and began sheeting him. And then Clover and Paul Brandt entered the operating room. Paul talked to the nurses, and Clover went to the head of the table and spoke to Mieslau.

A few minutes later, Clover and Brandt stepped up to the table. Brandt took the surgeon's place. And Clover stood across from him to assist.

"Did I call it, or did I call it?" Lou Manx said. "He just handed Paul the ball."

Paul had some discussion with the anesthetist. I guessed that it was about the patient's temperature. Mieslau's body temperature would be lowered to 28° centigrade in order to slow the metabolic needs of his body during the period when the heart would not be beating.

Apparently they came to agreement. Paul held out his hand, and the scrub nurse slapped a scalpel into it.

Paul made a T-shaped skin incision. Then, with Clover assisting, he split the sternum. After that, it seemed as if everybody in the operating room held his breath as they put Mieslau on the bypass machine.

It was all going smoothly — as was expected. I wished that they weren't all in masks, so that I could have seen their faces. I did wonder — and strongly — if they were involved in a political act as well as a medical operation.

Paul made a transverse incision at the base of the aorta. The valve could now be seen clearly. Next, he began filling the coronary arteries with oxygenated blood, which he pressed from a plastic bag.

There was a pause after that — a satisfied one. It was going perfectly. Then Paul asked for and received a pair of scissors. He started to cut out the valve — and that was when it happened. Maybe it was because he was rusty, having spent more time of late in the research lab than at the table. Or maybe it was because he, too, had heard all the rumors, and the pressure had become too much for him.

Whatever the reason, he slipped. The scissors cut one of the heart muscles. It wasn't a serious mistake. The damage was easily repairable. But it *was* a mistake.

And that was the end. Clover didn't acknowledge

the error. That is, he didn't say anything. But he did take the operation out of Paul's hands.

"To the showers," I heard Lou Manx murmur.

Clover repaired the cut in the heart muscle. Then he took the scissors and began removing the heart valve. From then on, Paul was an observer.

When it was over, Manx and I walked out together. I didn't say anything. And Manx was uncharacteristically silent. Then, while we waited for an elevator, Manx said, softly, "I'm with you — it stinks."

I had about a half-hour before I was scheduled to scrub. I left Manx when we got to our floor and went to one of the visitors' lounges. There, I used a pay phone and called Sue and told her what had occurred.

"Poor Paul," she said. "He must feel terrible."

"I don't know," I said. "Under normal conditions, he would have no reason to. Hell, things like that happen. Nobody was hurt. But I guess this wasn't a normal condition. That's the thing — I don't know."

There was silence for a second. Then she said, sounding tired of the subject, "Well, come home as soon as you can. I'm having liver. And I need you to peel that skin off."

"Isn't it about time you learned to peel that damn skin off yourself?"

"With a surgeon in the house? Why should I?"

So I hung up and then went up to scrub.

Fourteen

AN AIR OF suspense hung over the surgical floors during the next couple of days. No one talked about it to me

— except Lou Manx, of course. But I felt it. And I observed it. I noticed that when I was talking to one of the other doctors, he would be watching me rather than listening to me. I don't know what the hell they were looking for. For me to light up and spell out 'Tilt,' I suppose.

I wondered if Paul Brandt was being subjected to the same thing. But I couldn't track him down and ask him. And we didn't happen to run into each other. So I did the next best thing. I asked Lou Manx.

"We've talked about it," Lou said.

"I'll bet you have."

"He's taking it pretty much in stride," Lou said. "About the same as you, I guess. He doesn't care much for it. But what can he do?"

"Did Clover say anything to him?"

Lou shook his head. "I don't think so. I asked Paul, and he said no. Why would he lie about it?" He shook his head again. "No, I guess Clover kept shut about it. You have to figure it this way. It could have happened to anybody. It could even have happened to Clover. It fouled his plot, but he couldn't mention that."

"When is it going to pop?" I said.

"Soon. Hell, it has to be soon."

I got a message to report to Clover's office in the research building. When I opened the door, he was at his desk, occupied with some papers, which he was skimming through, then signing. He motioned for me to have a seat.

I guessed that this was it — that he was going to say something about the fellowship. But I wasn't in any sweat about it. By then, I had become a little numb to the subject. It had — I thought — become too important to too many people for the wrong reasons.

Finally, he pushed the papers aside.

"You're aware of our sixth year surgery fellowship," he said. He looked pained; it was obvious that this wasn't a pleasant task.

I said, yes, I was aware of the fellowship. "As a matter of fact," I said, "we talked about it a few weeks ago." Why the hell should I let him play games with me?

"Yes, that's right. We did speak of it — briefly." He turned slightly in his swivel chair, showing me his profile. "I believe I mentioned that I saw no reason why the fellowship shouldn't be used to encourage research."

"Yes, you said that."

"I haven't changed my mind," he said. "However, when making any decision, there are always —" He gestured vaguely with a hand. "— other elements that have to be considered. That is, elements other than the, uh, basic, uh, element."

I felt a little sorry for him. A *little*, but not enough to help him out.

"I asked the surgeons for recommendations," he went on. "Of course, this is *my* decision to make, but I value advice. Especially in, uh . . ." He locked his hands together and leaned back, making an effort to relax. "My point is, sometimes the attendings are closer to the house staff than I am. So, naturally, I like to hear what they have to say."

"Yes, sir."

"On the other hand, one hundred thousand Frenchmen *can* be wrong," he said.

"Pardon?"

"The majority makes mistakes, too," he said. "So, in the final analysis, the decision I make has to be *my* decision. You understand that."

I nodded.

171

"I have had it pointed out to me," he said, "that the intent of the fellowship program is to provide an extra year of study for a surgeon who intends to practice. Not that it had to be pointed out to me. I was aware of it. But, be that as it may, it *was* pointed out to me. Consequently, a great deal of thought has gone into this decision."

I edged a little forward, thinking that now, finally, he was going to say it. But . . . not yet.

"A great deal of thought," he went on, "because my natural leanings are toward research. I've always looked at it this way: One surgeon, standing at the table, performing one operation, can save one life. But one researcher, with one breakthrough can save thousands of lives." He smiled fleetingly. "You can't argue with numbers."

I leaned back.

"I am a surgeon," he said. "And I am a researcher. But." He swiveled back toward me. "But, it is important to my research that I am a good surgeon. Do you follow that?"

"I think so." I followed it, all right. But I wasn't sure that it was true.

"All this," he continued, "has had an effect on the decision I've had to make. "It has been made clear to me that a good surgical researcher should be, first, a good surgeon. Do you see?"

"Yes. That's what you said."

"I want to make sure you understand that."

I nodded. "Yes, I understand."

He smiled again. "There's no reason why it should concern you greatly," he said. "It's not a problem you'll have to meet, since you intend to limit yourself to practice."

I detected a dig in that word "limit."

He leaned forward, resting his elbows on the desk. still smiling. "What I'm getting at," he said, "is that I intend to recommend that you be awarded the fellowship."

I had waited so long that when it came I almost missed it. Perhaps I had stopped really listening to him. Anyway, it was a second before I realized exactly what he had said. Then, I didn't have an immediate reply.

"I'm sending the recommendation to Dr. Mackey today," Clover said. "But I wanted to tell you first. It occurred to me that you might not *want* the fellowship."

I gave him a silly grin.

"You *do* want it?"

"Yes."

"Uh-huh. All right. I'll forward the recommendation then. It will be automatic after that. You'll be notified by Dr. Mackey. He has, I believe, a speech that goes along with the award."

"Thank you."

"Oh, no thanks necessary. You deserve the fellow-ship."

"Thank you."

He stretched out a hand. "Congratulations."

And that was it.

When I left Clover's office, I called Sue. She squealed, and then had to hear all about it, from first word to last.

The only other person I told was Lou Manx. He laughed. A good, loud, genuine, belly-hugging laugh.

When he stopped laughing, he shook his head, grinning, and said, "The son-of-a-bitch. He knows when to quit. I'll give him that — he knows when to quit."

"Meaning what?"

"He could have stuck to his guns," Lou said. "He has the power. But he had sense enough to do it."

"I don't get what you're getting at."

"Listen," he said, "to get to the top — where Clover is — you have to survive along the way. There's a time to fight, and a time to give. This was a time to give. If he'd stuck to his guns, after all that happened, those surgeons would have climbed on his back and hung on until they dragged him down. He had sense enough to give, that's all."

"Isn't it just possible," I said, "that he figured he'd made a mistake, and he thought it over and decided to do what he believed was right?"

Manx looked at me pityingly. "Nothing that simple has happened since the age of Queen Victoria," he said. "We live in a complicated time. You better learn that."

The following day, I was summoned to Dr. Mackey's office. He *did* have a speech that went along with the award. He delivered it by rote, while taking telephone calls.

The day after that, the official announcement was posted. And that afternoon I learned that Lou Manx had invited everybody who knew me even slightly to a party in my honor at my apartment. It was a "bring your own" party. So, Lou informed Sue, all we would have to provide was a few bags of potato chips.

There were about a half-dozen guests — including Lou Manx — already there when I got home that evening. By ten, the place was so packed that it was almost impossible to move from room to room. Fortunately, Peter was at the Bruner's with their kids and a baby-sitter.

Paul Brandt came. He congratulated me — and

seemed to mean it. Then he mingled. And a few minutes later I saw him in conversation with Lou Manx.

Surprisingly, Dr. Gar also dropped by. He stayed for about ten minutes, looking happily sour all the while. He talked to Sue most of the time. When he left, I asked her what he had had to say.

"Nothing," she replied. "He told me how much he disliked parties — which amounted to nothing."

About two in the morning, the apartment started clearing out. Soon there was a steady rush for the exit. And by two-forty-five only Sue and I and Lou Manx were left. Sue and I were a bit fuzzy-tongued by then, but Lou appeared to be as sober as when the party started. Not because he hadn't been drinking, but because he had a way of keeping his balance throughout anything and everything.

"Did you talk to Paul?" Lou asked.

"A couple words."

"He didn't tell you about Boston?"

"What about Boston?"

"Clover has arranged for him to take a year of general surgery in Boston," Lou said, smiling. "Then, at the end of it, he's going to recommend him for the fellowship here. It's costing them a year, but they're going to get what they want."

"Won't there be the same trouble?" Sue said.

"Maybe. But I doubt it. Clover gave in when it was his turn. Next time it will be Gar's. I suspect they'll play the game."

"I hope so," I said. "That's the thing I hated most — cutting Paul out."

Lou grinned. "That makes it unanimous. Everybody's happy," he said. "You're happy, Gar's happy, the surgeons are happy, Clover is happy, and Paul is happy. Clover handled it very well. I admire the man."

"I just wish it hadn't happened," I said. "It takes something away from it."

"You can't get away from conflict," Lou said. "There just isn't any place to hide. The thing to do is recognize it and handle it. That's the important thing — to handle it, to handle it well. And Clover did it." He saluted. "Don't forget me when you throw your next party."

"Just let us know when it is," Sue said.

When Lou Manx left, Sue and I sat up until dawn talking. We hashed it all out. But even after all the talk, I still wasn't sure. Did it happen the way Lou Manx insisted it did? Or was it all in his mind — a crazy dream he'd managed to make us believe? Were Clover and Gar waging a political battle, or had Clover simply reached an unbiased, thoughtful decision?

I still don't know.